A collector's guide

Men!
A collector's guide

Jan Etherington

GRAPEVINE

First published 1989

© Jan Etherington 1989
Cartoons by MacLaughlan

British Library Cataloguing in Publication Data

Etherington, Jan
Men!: a collectors guide.
1. men. Interpersonal relationships with
women, — Humour
I. Title
305.3'0207

ISBN 0-7225-1900-1

Grapevine is part of the Thorsons Publishing Group,
Wellingborough, Northamptonshire NN8 2RQ

Printed in Great Britain by Richard Clay Limited,
Bungay, Suffolk

1 3 5 7 9 10 8 6 4 2

Contents

About The Author

J an Etherington is a freelance journalist and script
writer. She lives and works in London with her
husband, two teenagers and beautiful English Setter.
She has published showbusiness interviews and articles
on the funnier side of life in newspapers and magazines
including *Cosmopolitan*, *She* and *New Woman*.

With her husband, Gavin Petrie, she has written several
television and radio comedy scripts. In 1987 they won the
UK *Radio Times* Comedy Award.

In her spare time, she ignores the ironing.

Foreword

by Tim Brooke-Taylor

I think most of us are aware of the perils of dipping into a medical dictionary. Within minutes we are suffering from several fatal diseases, one of them previously thought to have died out in the 18th century, and another, usually only detected in white mice. So it is with this very dangerous volume '*Men! A collector's guide*'!

By my reckoning, I'm a nouveau chauvinist, athletic supporting, square-eyed, know-it-all, unromantic monster. I'd quite like to be collected as a Champagne Charlie but I don't think the Mr Mean in me would allow it.

Occasionally, Jan Etherington asks too much of us. The square-eyed sports watcher in me objects, rightly so in my opinion, when asked to get up and switch off just as Seve has an eight foot put for the Open or Steve Cram starts to make his move on the final bend. Anyway, I've always been convinced the Match of the Day music is a powerful aphrodisiac for most women! Most women who *collect* men, that is.

I'm not a gardener but my sympathies are with their so-called impossible dream. Even I might find I've got a privet to prune when faced with the bossiness of 'I thought we'd call and see Mother'. On the other hand, I am with the author when she claims that 'Real Men consider running is just walking hysterically.' But are we absolutely certain we don't want to be like the impossible men collected here? Put it this way, what if there were a companion volume on impossible women? There would be the Rich Bitch, the Blue Stocking, the Nympho, the Tease. But add them together and what have you got? Can I have two please?

Impossibility of course, is in the eye of the beholder. I've played a lot of impossible men in comedy shows and am quite flattered when strange women come up to me and bash me with their handbags. But when recently I played a very possible man, Tom in 'You Must Be The Husband', I never got the credit for being domesticated — apparently because 'he's not true to life'. It appears Adolph Hitler is more credible than Albert Schweitzer.

Our only hope as men lies in the knowledge that most heroes of romantic fiction start out not as mere difficult men but right bastards. Strangely, by page 200, these defects are now counted attributes — 'Oh Roger, you're so forceful'!

This, therefore, is an extremely useful guidebook, not for women, but for men.

Athletic Supporter

You must have met him at a sporting event. Did he tread heavily on your foot in his excitement when United scored? Shower you with froth from a much-shaken beer can when Ireland scored against Wales at Cardiff Arms Park? Or, on a higher plane, did you

trample the divets together between chukkahs at Windsor Polo Ground? However you met, two cheers for the Athletic Supporter. He loves sport. Sometimes one sport in particular but, mostly, any sport.

Because of his 'little problem' he doesn't play himself these days but he makes up for it by watching anything and everything. If he can't be in the stands or at the track, he watches it on television.

If there's a test match on, you can swing from your Tiffany lampshade wearing nothing but a pyjama cord and a broad smile and he won't even blink in your direction. When Steve Davis is about to pot the winning black, you can scream like a banshee that you've fallen down the back steps and you think your leg is broken in three places and he'll murmer 'Hang on, love, be with you in a minute, wait 'til Steve's got it safely in the pocket.'

And as for golf. You can write off whole weeks of your life when there's a major golf tournament on. If he can, he'll become a Gleneagles groupie or trudge around behind Seve Ballesteros at Lytham St Annes, hunched beneath a yellow umbrella. There he sits, the *Sporting Life* on his knee, glued to Racing From Ascot on his personal stereo. 'Look who's here!' you announce, bursting up on him. 'Your long lost cousin who's just navigated the Amazon, swum the Atlantic and crawled on her hands and knees up the hard shoulder of the M23 in order to get here by teatime to see you!' 'I'll come and say hello when I've heard the result of the steward's enquiry on Royal Gait,' he responds, without looking up.

You've not seen too many standard tourist sites on your holidays together and friends are a little bemused when you bring out your holiday snaps. Remember the two week tour of European soccer stadia? The walking holiday — round the golf courses of Scotland — and the 'magical mystery tour' to the crown green bowls final.

The fights you have if you have to go anywhere during the World Cup. 'But it's Spain vee Honduras!' he'll groan. Who cares? The Athletic Supporter doesn't even know where Honduras is but he knows the name of their star striker and how many goals they need to stay in the tournament. But you insist on dragging him away to visit friends. He spends the whole journey trying to tune in to the commentary on the car radio and, as soon as he's said a cursory 'hello' to his hosts, he manages to get the conversation round to football. 'Did you know it's Spain vee Honduras this evening?' 'Is it, begod?' says his host, without too much interest, because he is a normal person.

'You haven't got a telly in your spare room, have you?' pursues your Athletic Supporter relentlessly. And off he goes.

He knows you're not going to smack his legs in public and say 'Don't be so damn rude! Doreen and Kevin have got salmon sandwiches and Madeira cake for us. Get down here!' But wait 'til you get him home! Trouble is, when you do get him home, he's got to catch the tail end of the German Grand Prix . . .

He'll argue Arsenal's scoring record endlessly in the pub, he'll never tire of defending Botham, moaning about McEnroe, or discussing the mechanics of Mansell's move to Ferrari. He tried painting the living room ceiling when the Olympics were on and he's never stopped telling everyone, since the accident, that he uses the same physiotherapist as Queen's Park Rangers.

One Athletic Supporter's support claimed that her husband proposed to her just as the players were coming out on *Match Of The Day* but when she started to give him her answer, he told her to shut up 'til half time. Why did she say yes?

Treatment

Instead of Hoovering and asking him to lift his feet during the deciding penalty of the Cup Final and grizzling that you think Silverstone is the pits and cricket has you stumped, appear mysteriously in an off-the-shoulder jersey two piece and a haze of Chanel just as he's settling down to the darts tournament and announce that you've got an appointment. With any luck, he'll leap to his feet and sob, remorsefully, that he's been neglecting you. But I wouldn't give you more than evens.

Technoprat

Here's a test to see if you've landed a Technoprat. Just ask him the time. If he's still wearing a digital watch and *isn't ashamed of it*, you've got one.

Chances are, he wooed you on the phone. Probably his car phone. 'I'm just coming off the M1. I'll be in town

Darling, according to the computer, you left me two days ago.... Darling?.....Darling?....

in an hour. Fancy dinner tonight?' You manage to make out those sentences just about, what with all the crackle, because he bought a cheap one. But it's glamorous, isn't it? Well, before you say yes, imagine the future.

Back at his place, there's wall-to-wall technology. He's got a microwave, a digital alarm clock that does everything but iron the sheets, a video full of fitness exercises that's on a timer to get him up in the morning and, naturally, a multi-functional personal organizer with a storage facility of up to 288K, whatever *that* means in real money.

Anyway, to say he's fond of his computer is like saying Romeo seemed keen on Juliet. He's welded to his computer. He's got a portable one that he'll bring round to your place if he's staying overnight and he'll spend longer planning its programmes than he will on finding out what you'd like to do for the evening. He keeps telling you it's 'compatible'. 'Do you mean we're not?' you snap, 'Are you getting at me?' He disappears for days to play with it.

He's the mug that always buys everything new as soon as it comes on the market. The first on his street with a record player years ago, now he's got a CD player and a digital radio cassette for the car. He can tell quality, he says. That's what you're paying for.

The problem with Technoprat is that too often he only absorbs half the information in the manual. Thus, you find him blackened and smoking one evening because he didn't follow the instructions on the microwave, or sobbing uncontrollably because the computer won't do what he's telling it to. Any salesman loves Technoprat to walk through the door. They know they can string off a load of unintelligible rubbish and Technoprat will nod and be impressed. Technoprat beeps as he walks. It's either his work bleeper, the digital eyesore on his wrist or his stress assessor telling him to calm down. It's like going steady with R2D2.

He's got a hologram in the loo, a video entryphone and his garage doors open by remote control. So, you begin to believe, do his arms. When he's away from home, he switches on a timer device so that the lights go on and the curtains are pulled automatically at a different time every night. In fact, what with the video and the cooker on automatic timer as well, there is more noise and activity in Technoprat's home when he's out, than when he's in.

He's got no time for anything old, in fact Milton Keynes is his idea of the perfect environment. His flat is high-tech and his furniture about as comfortable and relaxing as a round with Mike Tyson.

If you're a woman who's in tune with technology then maybe Technoprat is for you. But if, like most of us, you have an on/off affair with the microchip then you may feel that the current situation is designed to make sparks fly.

With so many electronic devices in his life, you will pretty soon discover that, far from making life easy and giving you more time together alone, you are forever opening the door to repairmen and you will have to conduct your courtship with a service engineer sprawled on the carpet re-wiring the super sensitive magic eye of the burglar alarm.

Treatment

If you're trying to wean him off micro-dependency and back to the world of the Mickey Mouse alarm clock and the hand whisk, good luck. You'll have to break his circuits and leave him rusting quietly in the corner while you recharge your batteries and decide whether there is *anything* about Technoprat you could describe as user-friendly, or if it's time to punch the exit key on his module.

The Literary Lamebrain

Doesn't he look Nietzsche, you thought when you first saw him, in his cords and tweed jacket with the patched elbows. Add to that the Vyella shirt and wire-framed specs, and he's actually extremely fashionable, although he doesn't know it, and would be

amazed if you pointed it out. The chances are you ran into him at a library or an art gallery, or maybe you saved his life by dragging him out of the path of a cement mixer while he was ambling across a dual carriageway with his nose in a book. He probably said something terribly provocative when you met, like, 'Would Picasso have been so prolific if he had been born a Glaswegian?' You frowned with the effort of responding and came up with, 'Or if he'd had to hold down a day job?' For some reason, he thinks this is wildly funny and before you know it, he's reading you Thomas de Quincey in his book-lined garret. You feel a bit like Marilyn Monroe must have felt when she was swept off her stilletoes by the intellect of Arthur Miller.

There's no doubt that Literary Lamebrain is very clever and he knows the right words for everything. His friends are intimidating because they swap aphorisms across the dining table and toss references to Camus, Brecht and Aphra Behn to and fro as easily as the salad. You want to ask for the salt but it doesn't seem much of a contribution to the debate on Yeats' symbolism.

He can Name That Quote in one, and give you the play and the line from which it comes, but ask him to unblock a drain or change a tyre or a plug and he shows the brainpower of a daffodil. Literary Lamebrain will leave the grill on, the bath running and the keys in the front door. He'll go out for a loaf of bread and be found hours later, huddled in the corner of a bookshop deep in Diderot, oblivious to the emergency services you've summoned.

You'll come home after a hard day and he'll be stretched out on the sofa browsing through Kant's *Critique of Pure Reason*. 'Why have you not peeled the spuds, my love?' you ask in a purely reasonable way. He'd forgotten the time. He leaps up straight away. It doesn't matter you say, flinging potatoes in the sink. He's *not* lazy, he's *not* being a slob, he's just absorbed, his mind is somewhere else. Who cares the reason? It's damned inconvenient! Literary Lamebrain is a daydreamer. He's no use to you if you want help with your tax form, a shelf putting up or the oil leak fixed in the car but, my goodness, he doesn't half write smashing poems in your birthday cards. He always reads in bed. Not just a page or two, but half a book. A big book *with no pictures*. You can never get comfy and you sigh and bounce about, hoping he'll take the hint and elbow Eliot for more earthly pursuits. You have to take the initiative in sex as in most mundane activities.

You'll have a wonderful life with Literary Lamebrain if you can spend your days in a leafy bower while the staff bustle about indoors. But if it's just you and him and a burst hot water tank at four in the morning you'll probably tell him, in rhyming couplets, that it's the end of this chapter of your life.

Treatment

Appear in front of him in a nightdress with an upholstery tassle giving your bosom a bit of uplift, whip his book away and suggest you re-enact the love story of Abelard and Heloise. The nice bits, before they got upset and pegged out.

On the other hand, tell him firmly that you've had enough culture for one day and how about a bag of chips and a double helping of *Dallas*? It might also amuse him if you hid his library tickets down your cleavage. On the other hand, it might not.

The Nouveau Chauvinist Prig

He just can't understand it. He married a perfectly nice, ordinary little woman (she did very well for herself, if you want the truth) who only wanted to stay at home, sort out his sock drawer and rear his children. Life was good. It had order. But then it started to change.

CHAUVINIST!...RESPECT ME! SEXIST PIG!..NOT A SEX OBJECT! NOTICE ME!...EQUALITY!

Bloody hormones!

The kids got older, and she went a bit funny. She started wearing boiler suits, going to rallies and swearing. When he bought her a co-ordinated set of G-string and baby doll pyjamas for Christmas, she flung them back, snarling she 'was not a sex object'. She was equal, she said and wanted a bit of damn respect.

Fair dos, he said and had a go with the duster. He even made a passable Sunday lunch to show willing. She could drive his car and open her own doors, she said. Right, anything to keep her happy, he thought. So he let the door go one day when she was behind him, and she cracked her knuckles and screamed blue murder. What can you do?

Now, would you believe it, she's got herself a little job, started wearing high heels and wants him to 'notice her'. He'll notice her all right! Everytime he comes home, he notices there's no tea on the table. You wouldn't credit it, would you?

The NCP sighs heavily, looming towards the barmaid's bosom at the golf club. 'I freely confess I don't understand women,' he leers. 'You used to know where you were with women. Then all of a sudden they get peculiar. It's hormones, you know.'

The Nouveau Chauvinist Prig is a confused man. He'd planned to go along with Women's Lib — at least, he went along with the bra-burning bit, know what I mean? 'Course she wanted a bit of a change. Understandable. But they've got to learn when enough is enough.' What's worse, he's got a daughter who wants to be a Page Three model. He's not having that, he says. 'No daughter of mine is going to expose her chest and be ogled.' He does, however, ogle the exposed chests of other people's daughters in expensive magazines and cheap newspapers. But that's different. Obviously.

NCP would be upset if you called him a chauvinist.
God knows, he tried to give the little woman what she
wanted. He tried 'til he was blue in the face and as long
as she asked nicely. You have to humour them. Now she's
left him for her assertiveness training counsellor. He'll give
her assertiveness! Damn sauce! He should have trusted
his instincts and kept her barefoot and pregnant in the
kitchen. They're all the same, don't know when they're
well off. What's more, she wants half the house in the
divorce settlement. That's a laugh! What's she *ever* done
to deserve half the house? Sat at home for twenty years,
running up phone bills, that's what.

Bitter? Course he's bitter! And he knows one thing . . .
It's giving them ideas that's caused all this. His mother
never wore high heels and had assertiveness training. She
always had Dad's dinner on the table and he never
wanted for a darned sock in fifty years. She went first in
the end. Tired heart, the doctor said.

Treatment

If you've landed one of these bruised and confused
Nouveau Chauvinist Prigs, and you *really* think it's
worth your time and patience to take on a man with
more hang-ups than the wardrobes at the Savoy,
then you'll have to lay down some pretty clear
guidelines and stick to them.

Tell him exactly what time you're going to be
home — and stick to it. If you're having a drink with
the lads, ring him and explain. Tell him he looks nice
in that crimplene safari suit. A compliment here and
there works wonders. Bring little gifts home with you

now and then — after shave, Grecian 2000, odour-
eaters. Remember, parity begins at home.

The Gardener

'You've got the most beautiful hanging baskets I've ever seen,' was probably how you opened the conversation and the door to a blossoming romance. It is, however, as you pretty soon discovered, no bed of roses being grafted to the Gardener.

He comes home from work and there you are, lips puckered up to welcome him but does he notice? Does he heck! He's straight out the back to the potting shed to check on his mesembryanthemums.

Every corner of your home is germinating. There are begonias in the bidet, tomatoes over the hot water tank and on the window sills, your knick-knacks are tossed aside to make room for what looks like minature Nissen huts containing precious seedlings.

You may have fallen for this quiet, patient creature who combines the strength to turn over a beetroot bed with the gentleness to prick out petunias but, in time, you'll realize he's not the man you thought he was when your crazy-paving paths first crossed. He's a lot muddier for a start and his idea of excitement is the arrival of a new seed catalogue. You might think golf widows have a hard time of it, but at least they can meet up for a drink at the nineteenth. Gardening widows have *no social life at all* — unless you count humping a bag of fertilizer back from the garden centre with the Saturday boy pushing the trolley. And when you get back, there's no gratitude: 'I *said* John Innes No. 2!' Can plants count? Do they *know* what number it is? You will get a withering look, something gardeners are good at.

Weekends with the Gardener are a complete washout. 'I thought we'd call and see mother,' you suggest. 'I've got the privet to prune,' he responds, as if everybody knew that. And if you ever do get him out of the garden, it's embarrassing because he never goes anywhere without his secateurs or his cuttings knife. Thus, you are strolling down a leafy lane admiring the view, when suddenly, he'll stop and hiss, 'Just keep walking. There's a bit of mallow here I fancy.' You will be forced, unwillingly, into the role of lookout while he nicks a cutting and returns home with a pocketful of severed specimens, desperate to get at the rooting compound. Not only will he lead you into a life of crime, but there's no reasoning with the Gardener. A ruthless breed, your suggestion that you'd like a nice straggly herbaceous border is met with a look of shocked disbelief. The Gardener is convinced he can improve on Mother Nature's rather casual attitude to the plant kingdom. He's not having leaves flinging themselves towards the sun just where they feel like it. Nice straight lines with all the pansies facing the same way, and definitely *not* straggly.

There are advantages though. The Gardener won't let anyone else cut the grass. This is good news for everyone who resents slogging up and down the lawn with a spluttering engine in perfectly good sunbathing weather. He did let you cut the grass once, but you managed to decapitate the last known specimen in the entire world of this pink geranium. At least, you'd think it was, the fuss he made.

As long as you keep a reverent silence during *Gardeners' Question Time*, and don't assume you can tell weeds from flowers you might be able to put down roots for the future. If ever he has an affair, it will be with an horticulturalist. 'Sandra's got a variegated *ficus benjamina*,' he'll say one day, with a faraway look in his eye. 'I can't say I've noticed,' you will cut him off, at the nodule. 'She's going to let me have a bit,' he smiles happily. *That's* when it's time you nipped it in the bud.

Treatment

Try wearing a leaf green skirt, a flowery blouse and a spot of Baby Bio behind your ears. Tell him you need some special nourishment, and he hasn't talked to you for ages. Stand in a bucket of gravel looking droopy. Alternatively, lie back and enjoy it, at least he brings you flowers.

Mr Know-It-All

He *always* knows best. You can bet your life that where two or three are gathered together discussing the way to install a cast iron fireplace, complete with tiles, stripped pine chimney piece and flue, Mr Know-It-All will have done it so many times, he could do it standing

on his head with his arms tied behind his back.

You can't tell him anything. Whatever you've done, he's done before. Wherever you've been, he was there — before the property developers moved in and spoilt it.

'Don't tell _me_ about Marbella!' he's apt to say, shaking his head in disapproval at the inoffensive little resort as some innocent holidaymaker attempts to give his personal impressions to Mr Know-It-All. 'Did you eat at Manuel's on the harbour?' he adds, tut-tutting 'I could have told you that'd lead to Montezuma's Revenge.' His standard response to any information is 'I used to have one of those,' even if it's a custom-built, rococo cage for twin opossums.

He's the most irritating person in the world. He stabs you with his finger and talks at you, with his face far too close for decency. That is, of course, unless you love him.

When you met, you probably thought it was very reassuring to be with someone who knew exactly where he was going in life and, more importantly, how to get there, avoiding the roadworks.

In fact, you probably met when you asked him for advice. Where the Chief Buyer's office was located, how you work the coffee machine, or whether this train stops at Dewsbury. He knows how to get from Exeter to Maplethorpe, how to get an oil stain out of an anorak and, probably, how to get a camel through the eye of a needle. We can only give thanks that Mr Know-It-All was not present when Christ encountered the Rich Man because it would be six to four on that he would have stood up and explained that of all the camels he'd come across, the best way to persuade them through the needle's eye was . . . and cause Our Lord to lose his thread.

At school, Mr Know-It-All was a swot, of course. He

had his hand up so often that he only had to squirt deodorant under one arm. Nobody was surprised that he wanted to be a traffic policeman.

It is absolutely useless trying to put one over on Mr Know-It-All, and you can bet your life if you're excited about something, he will dampen your enthusiasm quicker than a slap in the face with a wet lettuce.

'Oh, you've bought a Ford have you?' he'll say, darkly. 'Well, if you'd asked me, I'd have told you what you're letting yourself in for . . .' 'You'll buy nothing but trouble if you buy that house, take my word for it . . .'

If a car slows down at traffic lights, while he's walking his dog, he's likely to bang on the window and ask 'Lost, are we?' so eager is he to show off his local knowledge. You'll find Mr Know-It-All in information offices everywhere. They are also found in large numbers propping up public bars and in the House of Commons.

Treatment

If his supreme smugness and habit of saying, 'Take my word for it', even when you insist you haven't had an orgasm, is getting you down (and if it's not, it should be) pick him up on *everything*.

Whenever the opportunity arises, preferably in company, counter with 'That's a load of steamed bananas. I know a much quicker way to Watford/Manuel's is a perfectly good restaurant, you're thinking of Pedro's/the only thing you know about fireplaces is how to put your feet on them.'

It may not improve your relationship but you'll quickly become such a sparky and entertaining double act that you'll be much in demand for soirées, fork buffets and barmitzvahs.

The Square-Eyed Monster

Your chance interruption at the party where you met, caused your eyes to meet across a sparsely-populated room — and he immediately tuned in to your wavelength. 'Felicity Kendal!' you said, brightly, when you heard him asking someone who was that actress that

starred in the series about a woman living alone?

He noticed you for the first time and must have imagined you were the perfect mate for the Square-Eyed Monster. You were rather flattered, at first, that he wanted to spend all your time together locked in a passionate clinch on the sofa.

Ever wondered why you were always facing the wall? because he was riveted to the John Wayne movie, *Summertime Special, Eastenders*, or whatever else was on the box at the time.

He's a telly addict, a Square-Eyed Monster. He'll watch everything from *Sesame Street* to the Sunday service, and what you had in common when you first met is what's driving you apart now.

Suggest a stroll in the park one afternoon and he'll respond, petulantly, 'We'll miss *That's My Dog!*' Tell him you've invited the neighbours round for drinks and he'll snap, 'They'd better not turn up in the middle of *Coronation Street*.'

You've felt a rising tide of irritation over the bolted meals, the rush home for the start of *Emmerdale Farm, That's Life*, or *M.A.S.H*.

How on earth did he survive before the invention of the video machine. Did he ever leave the house? He comes straight in from work and switches it on. No 'How are you, my love?', not a bit of 'Sit down and let's talk about our day.' Just slump and stare. Even if it's halfway through a documentary on an analysis of the lyrics of Nana Mouskouri, he's gripped and apparently riveted in seconds. He answers only in monosyllables. A tip here. This is, in fact, the best time to impart major news items like I've bent the car/bought a goat for the front garden/fallen in love with the TV repairman. You find it infuriating that, after an intimate dinner out, designed to create a romantic ambience, you come back giggly and affectionate and suggest, dangling your slingbacks provocatively around the door, that you both go straight to bed. 'You go ahead, love,' he is wont to respond. 'I just want to catch the end of Newsnight.'

If you are ever, even occasionally, responsible for recording programmes for him on the video, you will know the meaning of real fear. 'How *could* you record Open University on irrigation in Namibia instead of *Neighbours*?!' he'll rant. '*Now* what am I going to do this evening?' Talk to me? Take me dancing? Play strip Scrabble? Eat asparagus in bed? No, sulk.

His idea of sparkling social intercourse over dinner with friends is a moan about the number of repeats on Saturday nights and the quality of game show hosts. 'What do you think of that young bloke that does whatsitsname?' he demands, sniffing his Bulgarian Merlot, like they do on the *Food and Drink Programme*. 'He means Les Dennis on *Family Fortunes*,' you translate, for the puzzled fellow diner, having heard this enviably penetrating opening line many times before. He talks about TV entertainers as if he knows them personally. 'That Griff Rhys Jones, he's a lad isn't he?' 'Michael Aspel's a nice bloke. Never see him upset.' 'Jimmy Greaves is looking older. No doubt about it.' One thing you know for certain about the Square-Eyed Monster, he gets more of a thrill pressing the buttons on the TV remote control than running his fingertips over any of your erogenous zones.

Treatment

Switch it off.

Mr Mean

'**B**ut you've already got a frock!'

If your partner is Mr Mean, you will recognize that familiar response every time you open a carrier bag and reveal a modest day dress that you had purchased at a quarter of its price in the sale — and only

after a long debate with yourself about your criminal extravagance. '. . . what do you want another one for?' is how the sentence ends, and your problems begin.

You've learnt to live with leftovers, turning the sides to the middle, scraping out the last of the marmalade, wasting not and wanting not. He always makes you feel guilty, doesn't he? What is it with Mr Mean? He's often not short of a few bob. In fact, he's so tight with his money, he'll even demand change from charity collectors. He resents paying full price for anything — a holiday, a car or a wedding. Which is why the promised 'carriage and pair' on your special day, collapsed two miles from the church and lost a wheel due to the fact that it had only just unloaded a ton of firewood from a previous client, and was forced to attempt a gallop, to make up time.

'We don't need new carpets,' he'll insist, as you arc in a graceful somersault, having tripped on one moth-eaten hole.

'Make do and mend' was his mother's motto, as he is always telling you. 'Your mother could spend all her days making do and mending because she didn't have a full time job!' you snap back. How can he make you feel guilty if you're earning your own money? I don't know, but he does. You begin to analyse financial outlay on anything from a bunch of flowers to having your legs waxed.

He'll come round the supermarket with you and make sure you buy the cheapest of everything. Then you'll have a jolly hour, on your return home, checking the receipt to make sure they've made no mistakes.

'Twenty quid!' he'll splutter into his chain-store mug of '20p off this week' coffee, when you came back from the hairdressers. 'We used to have a hair cut, buy a three piece suit, have a fish supper, a holiday in Scarborough

and still have change for a taxi home, for twenty quid!'
Little does he know you've been economical with the
truth. It was nearer thirty, what with the colour and perm
solution.

He won't throw anything away of course. The attic and
the shed are full of bits of wood, old chairs, dismantled
electrical items, all of which will 'come in useful'.

Mr Mean's home is often a strange assortment of
colours and styles. This is because, rather than follow a
designer's advice or compliment the proportions of the
house, he headed straight for the discount ads and special
offers in the High Street. Whichever paint's cheapest, even
if it's maroon, is what your hall will be and if there's a
cheap suite going at the Co-op, he'll push it home (he'll
never pay delivery charges).

Moving house with Mr Mean is one of life's more
embarrassing experiences. He'll take the doorknobs, the
lightbulbs and all the best plants from the garden. 'Wasn't
there an apple tree on the front lawn?' your purchasers
query when you meet them at the gate, on account of
being late leaving, while he's still unscrewing the draining
board. 'You must be mistaken,' says Mr Mean, trying hard
to stand in front of his car and obscure the fact that the
aforementioned apple tree is poking insistently out
through the sun roof. Who'd be seen with Mr Mean?

Treatment

Act meaner than him. Buy him gristly bits of meat
for a week because you're 'cutting down'. Tell him the
bath water's cold because you've turned off the water
heater. Explain that the last thing you can think
about is all the expense of two days in a caravan at

Westcliff after that last gas bill.

Wear your oldest frock to a 'do' and make sure the seam rips as he dips you in the paso doblé. And if all else fails, buy him a Labrador. However mean he is, nothing will be too much for him to spend on food and home comforts for his precious dog. In no time at all, you'll reap the benefits — as long as you like Bonio.

The New Man

The New Man knows more about PMT than you do. He understands what it's like to be a woman because he's read all the books.

'Feeling a bit pre-menstrual?' he'll say, smiling understandingly, as a recently flung tuna and mushroom

pizza whistles past his ear. He'll be out buying you zinc tablets and vitamin B_6 before you can say Claire Rayner. New Man is thoughtful and caring, never leaves his socks on the floor and always cleans his teeth before making love.

The New Man has deep contempt for the rest of his species. All those impossible bores who go off down the pub, play rugby on Saturdays call their wives 'Er Indoors' and think equality is letting her watch Dynasty every week without moaning.

On Saturdays, New Man is down the supermarket with a carefully hand-written list. He'll never forget the air freshener for the loo. 'After all,' he reasons, quite often and quite loudly at parties, 'Why should Melissa have to slog around Sainsbury's on her own when we both work? It's only fair that we share the household duties.'

Trouble is, he's better at it than you. He does things like skirting boards and picture rails even when it isn't April. He practically shoves you out of the kitchen because he makes a cheese soufflé to die for. He'll bring you flowers every Friday and thinks it's a great idea that you keep up with your girlfriends and go out on the razzle at least once a month. He even manages not to sound patronizing. He smells better than you do. He never makes demands or throws accusations at you. You'll never hear New Man grizzling that he hasn't got a clean shirt. He's ironed them all on Sunday evening and probably pressed your blouse and skirt as well. He never gets drunk or rolls home late because he 'respects you too much'.

Even making love, New Man is disturbingly considerate, as anxious to please as a local councillor up for re-election. He will move painstakingly over your erogenous zones, no short cuts, no rush, nookie by numbers. He wouldn't dream of forcing himself on you. That would be a violation.

Mothers love him. They call him a real gentleman because he always helps with the washing up and says they've 'done enough, cooking that marvellous lunch'. In fact, he's better with your mother than he is with you, in many ways.

So why does the helpmate of this paragon feel vaguely uneasy?

Is it because she has nothing to rebel against?

Treatment

Oh, for heaven's sake! Don't be so picky! All right, so, every now and then you do feel your relationship is too good to be true and it's rather like getting on with your parents when you're 16 — almost unheard of. But if ever there was a man close to being a Perfect Man it's New Man. Some women are never satisfied.

The Endangered Species

Misogynist is much too glamorous a name for the Endangered Species. He'd probably be quite flattered by the title, once he'd looked it up. Brainless prat is nearer the mark.

His view, and he'll announce it to anyone who can't run

fast enough, is that men are an endangered species and
he, for one, won't have any woman running his life. He
makes love with about as much grace as a drunk falling
into a percussion kit.

He's in favour of men's clubs, strip joints, stag nights
and filthy jokes. He has a Playboy Club sticker on the
back of his car and probably a sign saying 'Sex Lesson —
please see driver' as well. He probably went to a single
sex school and is a clone of the father who treated his
wife like a servant and, when she timidly announced she'd
booked driving lessons, was so scathing about the very
idea that she sobbed for a week and gave up the idea of
being an individual forever.

His views of women are contained in two sentences.
Either 'She's a bit of alright,' or 'She's an old cow'. His
views of women drivers are contained in one sentence —
'They shouldn't be allowed on the road.' You can always
tell the Endangered Species by the way he drives. He
drives like there was no tomorrow — and there isn't, at
least not for anyone who gets in his way.

The Endangered Species hates women in any position
of power, but especially behind the wheel of a car. The
reason he drives like a maniac is to try and frighten them
off the road. It is also because he is an appalling driver. If
there is a woman in front of him, he will lean on the
horn, just because she is female. He will then overtake her,
engine screaming, shaking his head in patronizing disbelief
that she was not prepared to drive at seventy over a
school crossing in the High Street.

If you are unlucky enough to be manacled to the wrist
of the Endangered Species, you'll be used to the continual
snide remarks and public put-downs about everything
from your driving to your brushwork on the skirting
boards. Whatever did you see in him?

We'll give you the benefit of the doubt and say that while the balance of your mind was disturbed, you mistook his rudeness and bad manners for masculinity. Doubtful, but it's your only excuse. You probably thought his driving was a bit hairy but you could cope with it, if you closed your eyes and clamped a personal stereo over your ears to blot out the bad language.

The only reason why the Endangered Species is not yet extinct is because no woman with any sense at all cares about him enough to tell him exactly what she thinks of him. If he ever gets close enough to a woman who is confident and not prepared to be addressed as 'darlin', in other words, if the lift doors close before she can get out, he becomes a complete fawning idiot, desperately trying to steer the conversation into the caveman school of courtship. Naturally, she'll look at him as if he's recently been rescued from a vat of rotting compost and, once she's stepped out of the lift, he'll announce to disinterested fellow travellers, 'She was crazy about me. You could see it, couldn't you?'

He gasps as he says it because, in her departure, she has planted a stilleto heel firmly on his toe.

All car mechanics are Endangered Species, all staff in DIY shops, woodyards, train drivers and every salesman in the whole world. Oh, and any man found on a building site, of course.

Treatment

As he doesn't think women have any intelligent contribution to make, he won't listen if you tell him that he's in danger of dying out unless he becomes a nicer person. You'll have to find another man to tell him. So find one and leave him. He'll tell the world you 'couldn't stand the pace'.

Bachelor Boy

It all seemed so perfect at first. He was calm, sensible, intelligent, the kind of man you'd want to spend the rest of your life with. But one thing's for sure, with Bachelor Boy, it won't be a married life.

He wasn't, you thought, the kind of man to lead you

up the garden path. You were right. He hasn't led you anywhere very much. You liked the fact that he was in command, he didn't get angry or overwrought. He didn't get possessive or make demands on you. Be honest, though, he didn't get anything at all, really, and, especially, he didn't get married. He likes his own company, his job's going well and he's got his flat just the way he wants it. He seems completely self-contained and he doesn't miss you when you're not there. He's a good cook and, if you're at his place, he does all the cooking. He uses things like fennel and okra and takes it all very seriously. What's more, he puts things away. He's very tidy and your habit of leaving crisp packets beside the bed and putting your feet on the glass-topped table, shifting his collection of shells from the Bahamas, causes him to clench his teeth and frown at your extremities.

Bachelor Boy hates kids, they leave fingermarks everywhere and stare at him far too honestly. He is very unlikely to have a close friend. He's certainly never felt the need to confide in anyone and when you ask him if everything's all right, he'll say, 'Of course, why shouldn't it be?' Often he seems miles away and he accepts your carefully chosen presents, like the handsewn sampler with his name in cross-stitch or the card you made for his birthday, with enigmatic good manners but thinly disguised indifference. It's always *you* who rings *him* and he's neither surprised nor apparently thrilled to hear your voice.

The only time you'll encounter anything approaching emotion is if you start home-making. Buy him a set of sheets or some attractive wine glasses and you'll notice a vein start to throb in his neck. There is nothing of yours in his flat and if you leave 'by mistake' a scarf, a book or an uplift bra at his place, you'll find it returned by messenger before you can pick up the phone and suggest you call and collect it.

Women who get entwined with Bachelor Boy have often been 'engaged' for anything up to half a century. You probably bought the ring yourself and wear it on your middle finger when he's with you because he has a pathological fear of not only marriage but even walking on the same side of the road as a jeweller's shop. It's absolutely no use pretending to be pregnant to get him to the Registry Office door, because he'll hate you forever for trapping him. You begin to think he doesn't really need you at all. And you'd be right.

Treatment

If he doesn't need you, try and make sure he wants you. Adopt the persona of Bachelor Girl, even if your instincts are to stay sobbing by the 'phone. If it rings, don't answer it. Don't be there. Tell him you've got to go to Brussels and ask him to water your plants. Stay at your mother's. Alternatively, tell him that you understand from a recent report that determined bachelors often have a low sex drive. That might do the trick. When in doubt, hit below the belt.

The Workaholic

L iving with the Workaholic is like living with Jehovah. The only sign of his presence at home is a strong white light around the study door. You should have seen, or, at least, heard it coming but it seems that love is not only a blind but deaf, in your case.

There you were, gazing into each other's eyes and listening to his voice. You were so busy maintaining an intelligent yet melting expression that you didn't actually hear that he was not whispering sweet nothings but describing sewage systems I have loved. You had another chance to hear the warning sounds of the Workaholic when he took you out to that romantic little restaurant. There was, you observed, a faraway look in his eye. Was this the night he would propose? 'If they shifted that parlour palm and moved the aspidistra behind the piano, they could get three more tables along that wall,' he blurted out. 'Makes sound economic sense, wouldn't you say?' You're disappointed but you nod brightly. He doesn't notice. He is talking earnestly into the portable phone he had placed indiscreetly beside the breadsticks as you sat down. It rang a lot that night. Did any warning bells? If you live with a workaholic, it'll always be just the three of you — you, him and the 'phone.

You can always spot the Workaholic at parties. He is the one who, in answer to the seemingly innocent question 'And how many children do you have?', replies 'Two — Ow!' This is because his wife of several years has kicked him in the shins and hissed 'Three! You've forgotten Oliver!'

The partner of the Workaholic has warmed up more lasagnes than the local trattoria. She's given up slipping into a newly pressed frock and chilling a Martini at 7.30 on the dot. Now she's more likely to be slumped in front of *Eastenders* in a track suit, dipping into a box of assorted centres, knowing that he is unlikely to show before the late news. If he does appear, she needn't worry that he'll think she looks a mess. He won't notice. He'll come halfway through the door, a question on his lips. 'Did I leave a brown folder on the hallstand?' and

promptly U-turn back to the bypass, only the swaying
curtains betraying his recent presence.

She's been out to dinner alone more times than Greta
Garbo. 'John is in Cologne/Dubai/Neasden.' Wherever he
is, he's not *there*, not unless it's a dinner for clients.

The Workaholic almost always marries his secretary. If
not the first time, then the second or third. It saves time
because he knows she can organize everything from a
botany wool jumper for his mother's birthday to a dinner party
for twelve to include seven vegetarians, four carnivores
and a mystic who only eats diced carrots in honey.

The Workaholic is often multi-married, and some
would suggest that he is not a workaholic by instinct but
by the necessity of keeping up the alimony payments.
Now and then Mrs Workaholic will put her foot down and
insist he takes a holiday. He's reluctant, but finally agrees
to 'get away from it all'. It's only when she takes a call
from the travel agents, informing her, in answer to Mr
Workaholic's query, there *is* a Fax machine at the Hotel
du Soleil on the promenade, that she realizes she's taking
it all with her.

By day two of their holiday, he's 'had a little word' with
the bewildered pool attendant and suggested a far more
labour efficient way of distributing sun loungers and by
day four, he's produced a waterproof calculator from the
pocket of his swimming trunks and worked out the
number of pebbles on the beach. 'I'm just doing it for you',
he'll tell his partner. 'I don't *want* it done for me!' she'll sob,
as his company Sierra disappears down the drive at dusk
once more.

She's more jealous of his work than she would be of
another woman. That's because she hasn't met the other
woman. Yes, he's even got the energy to put in a bit of
overtime.

Treatment

What attracted you to him in the first place? His dynamism? His energy? His love of his work? Right. Well then, stop complaining and pass the coffee crème.

Married But Misunderstood

He'll edge a buttock chummily onto the edge of your desk, fiddle with your paperclips and confide, with just the right catch in his voice, that he finds it very easy to talk to you — and you've noticed it, haven't you? You haven't fallen for that tired old line, have you? The

My wife doesn't understand me...

But I do!

one about his wife not understanding him? Dear, oh dear.

Of course, it's such a neon-lit cliché that even he dare not use that phrase anymore, so he implies that you and he have 'a rapport'. He's more subtle, or he thinks he is. About as subtle as a car clamp.

He's not daft enough to criticize his wife so instead he suggests that he and she are so far apart in desires, interests and aspirations that you begin to wonder how they ever managed to agree on the colour of the curtains, let alone have three kids, a labrador and a two-storey extension.

'Beryl and I get on well enough,' he'll sigh, hitching the collar up on his denim leisure shirt and chloroforming you with enough after-shave to kill a llama, 'it's just that she's got her Zen Buddism/pottery/greyhound racing. There's not a lot of room for me in her life.' Pause for sympathetic murmur.

Are there blokes still around like Married But Misunderstood? And are there still women daft enough to fall for them? Yes to both questions.

'I booked an intimate little restaurant. Just the two of us,' a shuddering sigh. 'But she had to go to a school meeting.' He reaches for the Kleenex. Strange how he manages to make out that he's a caring devoted husband while pressing a hand urgently on your inner thigh.

'I feel as if I'm the only one fighting for our marriage,' he says. 'She doesn't care.' How *can* he be 'fighting for his marriage' when he's also fighting to release the button on the reclining seat in his car and have you, literally, fall in with his plans?

Married But Misunderstood will always give you his work number but, in spite of his 'We go our separate ways, have a completely open relationship and she doesn't mind what I do' line, if you ever phone him at home he will never, *ever* speak to you again. That is the rule. *His* rule.

What you have to understand is that, contrary to popular belief, the world is full of married men who *love* being married. Not only do they like their wives a lot but they also passionately love the security and stability of married life. The last thing they intend to do is jeopardize it. The problem is that they all have egos the size of Australia and a pathological need to flirt as well.

Do not be taken in by the tales of being married 'in name only' of separate beds, and of her harsh tongue and coarse habits. Ten times out of ten, if you ever meet Mrs M But M, she will be sexy, charming, and as much like the back of a bus as Meryl Streep. He's a creep. He lies about everything. No, he will not leave her for you, and he is not just waiting until the children are a bit older. He is waiting for you to push off.

If he's yours, then you will understand him very well. You are used to watching him grazing through the fields at parties; trapping a naïve young funster against the wall with one arm and a cloud of *Eau Sauvage*. You could repeat the conversation word for word. 'Yes, my wife's here, but we tend to go our separate ways . . .'

Treatment

If you're the third corner of Married But Midunderstood's triangle, get wise and get out.

If you're his wife and he's becoming even more boring and blatant than usual, and flirting not only behind your back but before your very eyes, then act. Choose your moment at the next party, walk up to him and his latest victim, wait for a pause in the disco rhythm and remind him loudly, 'It's time for your tablets, dear. He gets funny turns, you know. It's his age.' You'll probably laugh about it when you get home. Or he might run over you with the lawn mower.

The Confrontationalist

You probably met over a good row. Were you the traffic warden who slapped a ticket on his windscreen? The florist who, he claims, sent wilting weeds to his mother? Perhaps you were the shop assistant who refused to give him the money back on a pair of

two-tone brogues he insists he disliked before he's hardly unwrapped them, yet they smell suspiciously of athletes' foot powder.

He's the Confrontationalist. He goes through life waiting to be offended, short-changed, cut-up by fellow motorists, served mouse-droppings in his pizza and offered a diet of sex and violence by all the television channels. He's given them all a piece of his mind, make no mistake.

Maybe you thought that it was nice to find a man who wasn't afraid to stand up for himself and refused to take second best or second place. Well, it isn't that nice, is it? Everytime you go out to dinner, there's trouble. 'Call this a *linguini al funghi*' he bellows, 'Where's the mushrooms?' 'These peas are not fresh.' 'This steak is so rare it should be kept in a safe.' 'The sorbet tastes of soap.' Sometimes the refrain may be different but it's the same old tune. Waiters come skidding over with replacements and apologies but that's not enough to satisfy him. He wants to see the manager. We make the mistake of believing the Confrontationalist is a moralist and a perfectionist. He's nothing of the sort. He's an irritable little twerp who wants something for nothing, and tries to browbeat people into giving it to him. If there are other people with you, he feels constrained to act out the full scenario and demand a full meal for the traumatic experience of being given a scratched glass. 'Let me deal with it', is his motto but, boy, do you regret it if you do.

Move in with him and within a few weeks, you discover that you're blacklisted by all the local tradesmen. Every plumber, electrician and painter in the neighbourhood has been accused of incompetent and shoddy workmanship by the Confrontationalist, and retired a beaten and poorer man. 'I'm not paying for that,' he tells them all. If his plane is five minutes late departing, he's up there at the information desk banging on about loss of earnings due to missed appointments and writing a letter to the airline chairman before the plane has finished taxiing down the runway.

In fact, he's an expert at letters of complaint and he is proud of the fact that he's on first name terms with the trading standards officer of the local council. Mind you, the first name the council officer calls him is not terribly flattering.

His partner is usually nervy, living in constant fear of the next confrontation he engineers. He's rotten to visitors. Find yourself next to a Confrontationalist round a dinner table and he'll find something he doesn't agree with before you can say, 'Do you live locally?' 'How can you say privatizing the health service is a good thing?'. 'Taxi driver are you? Never look before you stop to pick someone up, I suppose.' 'Oh, so you're one of those softies who believe you should reason with criminals!' He lurks behind the festoon blinds just waiting to spring out in front of the unsuspecting paper boy and boom, 'And I will thank you not to scuff up my lawn with your bike!'

If he wants to have a go at you, he plans his campaign, chooses the words and even the position so you find him tense and thrumming in the big armchair as you burst in from a yoga class. He looks as inviting as a cold bath. 'Was this my white shirt?' he begins, waving a pinkish item before your eyes. 'Oh, I must have put it in with the red socks. Never mind,' you respond, because you have been calming your inner self and are not about to hit the roof. 'Never mind!' he splutters. 'That shows a fairly careless attitude to clothes, doesn't it?' 'Shut up, you old windbag!' is the only sensible response, followed by a swift exit to the bathroom but that may not be the end of it. He'll be snapping through the keyhole, angry at being deprived of

his confrontation . . . 'I seem to remember a pair of Y-
fronts going from yellow to grey last December . . .'

Treatment

Show him a health report that says over-agitation
weakens the heart. If you can't find one, write one. If
he starts arguing about it, tell him his lips are turning
blue. But only if he's worth fighting for.

The BMW Bore

The BMW Bore is all torque . . . and revs and carbs and electric windows. The BMW Bore believes it's not what you *are* but what you drive.

The keyring arrives first. Slapped down on the bar or your desk, inches from your nose. 'BMW' it says, in

BMW!

Bloody **M**ind **W**arping

unmistakable twinkling letters. He waits for your reaction. If you yell 'Some prat's dropped his keys!', you are immune to the power-assisted charm of the BMW Bore. But if you sigh 'Have you really got a BMW?' he'll ask you out for a drive.

If, however, you have any ideas about climbing into the back seat for a cuddle, forget it. You are never alone with BMW Bore. He's so proud of the car that he's always offering people lifts.

'We'll pick you up, it's on our way,' he'll offer, even though *you* know it's fifteen miles in the opposite direction.

You can't leave anywhere in a hurry with BMW Bore. If you've been to dinner with friends and they come out to say goodbye, you'll wave quickly and tell them not to wait.

'What's the engine capacity of this, then?' says the friend to the BMW Bore, frowning an interested smile at your man's dream machine. Your heart sinks to the colour-co-ordinated carpet. There follows an endless, rambling and paralysingly boring conversation on BMW engines after which you are snoring in your seatbelt while your hostess has long since made her apologies, nipped indoors, cleaned her teeth and put the lights out. He's saved up for this car. Worked nights. Stayed in. Missed holidays. Every weekend he'll clean and polish it. If you are planning to be Miss Helpful and bring him out a cup of tea during his labours, don't put it on the bonnet! His face will turn purple and he will chase you with the jack.

Everytime you go out, he will hear the faint noise under the bonnet that needs his attention. You can never hear it. If you think there might be a faint noise on the way, you turn the digital stereo up. He turns it off. 'Hear that!?' he frowns. 'That clunking sound.' 'That's because we've just run over a Coke can,' you snap. He is not easily convinced.

Like all car groupies, BMW Bore talks about his as if it was a woman. 'She's a great performer, never lets me down . . .' But he's got a central locking system on his emotions, except where the blessed car is concerned.

And like every groupie, he's always after the next conquest, the next one up in the range. The new model. His idea of a thrilling afternoon is a tour of the BMW showrooms with the odd test drive thrown in. 'You care more about that damn BMW 5 series than you do about me!' is an oft-heard cry from the partner of the BMW Bore. His reply is mortifying. 'I care more about the BMW 3 series than I do about you!'

Treatment

Admire a man in a Mini or, better still, a passing pedestrian. Tell him that all research indicates that men who idolize powerful cars are inadequate in other areas. Tell him it makes you carsick and if he loves you, he'll sell it. Personally, I wouldn't take the risk but then you probably have more confidence than me.

Superslob

There he sits on a Saturday afternoon — or any other afternoon, come to that — sprawled out on the sofa, lager can in one hand, fag in the other, belching in stereo and you ask yourself for the hundredth time 'wouldn't any jury in the land believe I had "just cause" if I

dispatched him with a sofa cushion?'

It was fun at first, the burping contests, chalking up for him on the dart board, the lie-ins in the morning. The thing was, you eventually got up to do mundane little tasks, like earn a living. He didn't.

If it wasn't his back playing him up, it was the fact that he came over all dizzy, he said, when he stood up. 'Could it be something to do with the eleven pints of beer you sank last night, O Light of my Life?' you observe with just a hint of sarcasm, as he demands a 'light' breakfast of bacon, eggs, sausage, beans, tomatoes and four rounds of toast. He is not so much work-shy as work-terrified. He walks round in a gravy-stained vest all day, stomach resting on his knees. His back view is a nauseating expanse of buttock cleavage.

If you suggest that he might like a bath or shower, his response is, 'Why? Is it your birthday?'

The idea that he might like to smarten up and learn a few social graces, like using a knife and fork, to earn the love of a good woman, is likely to be met by a blank stare from Superslob.

'I've always done alright,' he'll claim, dunking a pickled gherkin in his lager, 'no complaints so far.'

The reason why he's had no complaints so far is because most women don't know where to start. Listing his faults can take so long that by the time you've reached '. . . and another thing, did you have to wipe your bread round your plate at Martin and Sharon's dinner party?' he's snoring in the armchair with his mouth open, displaying a mouth like the decay posters in the dentist.

His idea of romance is to watch the sun sink over the betting shop with a bag of chips in his hand. 'Don't you want to look nice?' frowns his exasperated lady love. 'What for?' he grunts, 'Are we going on *Mr & Mrs*?'

Desperate partners of Superslob have tried sneaking him into shape by tipping mouthwash in his beer and preparing the odd salad for supper. They've not had much success. He's spotted the spiked beer and tossed the supper aside with the riposte, 'Salad's rabbit's food! What's for tea?' Then, just when you're prepared to leave him, he'll do something endearing like make you a chip butty for breakfast, with extra HP sauce and you think maybe you could do worse.

Treatment

Don't be wooed by a chip butty, you really *couldn't* do worse than Superslob. In a world of pressed denim and deodorant, he stands out like Pavarotti in a *corps de ballet*. Tell him you're tired of living with an overweight, unfragrant lout and if he jokes that he didn't know your mother had moved in, head for the door.

It might take six months or so but the next time he's looking for a clean shirt, he'll miss you.

Groovy Man

He was there at Woodstock, of course — although he doesn't tell you it's Woodstock, *Oxfordshire*, not Woodstock, USA.

He once had a conversation with Bob Dylan about the meaning of life, although Dylan can probably only recall

some hairy idiot blocking the doorway of the recording studio and shouting 'Hey! man!' and responding 'Hey! yourself!'

Groovy Man is still there, back at where it's at, welded in the Sixties, an elderly hippie with flowers in his hair and funny cigarettes in his tasselled shoulder bag. Long since past his 'sell-by' date, he's caught in a time warp. Wheelclamps and flavoured yoghurts mean nothing to him. He's still wearing an embroidered Afghan jacket which smells like a goat with halitosis, and he's the only man who thinks the racks of stacked heels, paisley shirts and flares in the charity shops are this year's desirable fashion buy.

He'll never see 35 again but he's got pierced ears and his hair is longer than yours. Beards are *de rigeur* for Groovy Man. Not the smart Sir Walter Raleigh kind but huge, bushy, face blankets often containing selected titbits from his last three meals and and a family of money spiders.

If he has a car at all, it'll be a Citroen dustbin-on-wheels covered in psychedelic painting and stickers from San Francisco.

Groovy Man still thinks orange is a cool colour and paints the ceiling of his 'pad' in navy blue. Come back to his place and you'll sit, or rather, squat with your legs crossed on a tangerine floor cushion while he sits with his legs crossed and listens to Velvet Underground, the Grateful Dead or the Doors with his eyes closed.

His idea of a holiday is to go back-packing to Stonehenge for the summer solstice or hitch a ride on the Marrakesh Express.

He's not into possessions — at least, not his possessions. He is, however, into everyone else's, especially their houses. Thus, he'll often 'drop in' on friends for a drink, and two or three weeks later prove more dificult to shift than the ring around the bath.

Groovy Man is into peace, love — and saving himself as much commitment as possible to real life. He claims he's a free spirit, floating hither and yon but let him get a whiff of your Posture Sprung bed and your well-stocked freezer and he'll be at your side 'til his flowers wilt.

Groovy Man is so laid-back, he's prostrate. He didn't exactly opt out because he never opted in. He has a certain colourful attraction, if you like hirsute, unwashed men in loose frocks and headbands but most women are suspicious of anyone who calls them a 'cool chick'.

Treatment

Buy him a Next suit and treat him to a haircut and shave for his birthday. He won't do it himself but if you do it for him, he'll be so stunned, he won't know himself. He'll start demanding a carphone and buying Glaxo shares. It's called growing up. Of course, not everyone wants to, but . . .

Bodge-It-Yourself Man

While other men may woo you with flowers or After Eights, Bodge-It-Yourself Man comes courting with an occasional table. He made it himself. Really? How clever!

Pretty soon you discover why these tables are called

'occasional', as you stick a folded envelope under one of the legs and try to polish out the glue stains. Almost without exception, they have been made by BIY men and should only be used very occasionally. Imagine BIY Man at the dawn of time. 'What this cave needs, Raquel, is a bit more space. Hand me that flinthead axe, love and we'll knock these two rooms into one.' Thus began the first man-made avalanche.

BIY Man believes that if a thing's worth doing, it's worth doing on the cheap. He'll never ever call in professional help. 'You don't need a plumber,' he'll say, as his wife wades through the kitchen in a diving helmet and wet suit. 'It's only a bit of water. I just need to solder this pipe.' BIY Man, for some reason, flocks to one profession above all others — the building trade. Surprise! Surprise! 'Who told you that you'd need an RSJ put in?' he'll chuckle, shaking his head at the very idea. 'Course you don't. Bit of plasterboard and Bob's your uncle. Oi! Charlie! Put the kettle on!'

Partners of BIY Man tend to be nervous, jumpy women. They turn the taps on with their fingers crossed and never stand under shelves. Often, for evening leisure wear, they choose a hard hat and a boiler suit. The memory of the night dash to casualty when the newly plastered ceiling fell down in the middle of *Dynasty* is still, literally, painfully fresh.

BIY Man and his mate eat breakfast on the move. This is because he didn't use a spirit level when he built the 'breakfast bar' and they have to keep pace with their scrambled eggs in the mornings as they slide inexorably towards the double drainer.

Drive down any street and you will see the mark of Bodge-It-Yourself Man as a blot on the landscape. That bricked-up window in startling contrast to the rest of the house, the peculiarly undulating front wall topped with sea shells, the porch that leaks and leans to starboard, all monuments to his mistakes.

BIY Man lives in a permanent building site. 'Bill's just extending the kitchen,' friends are told, as they clamber over the debris. 'I thought he did that last year?' they query. 'He did,' clenches Mrs BIY Man. 'He's doing it this year as well.'

Never buy a house from BIY Man, although we all have. In fact, never buy a house from anyone who says 'You can never have too many shelves, can you?' You can. One shelf is more than enough if BIY Man has hammered in the screws.

BIY Man calls the garden shed his 'workshop' and he'll disappear for days at a time, finally emerging with a strange object he claims is a dual purpose garden recliner and ironing board. 'What about me!' his partner will cry. 'I need some attention too!'

He'll rush back to the workshop and knock her up a 'vanitory' unit with three-way hinged mirror. He can't understand why she's not impressed.

Treatment

Look on the bright side. You're still alive, aren't you? He hasn't actually killed anyone, has he? On the other hand, as he's just unwrapped that Build-Your-Own-Sauna kit, it's only a matter of time, so get a real man in your life to pick up the pieces and put you back together again.

Champagne Charlie

Champagne Charlie is as expansive as a hot air balloon. His clothes are as noisy as his conversation. Bright checks, blinding ties and a hat clamped firmly on his head.

Champagne Charlie's first words were not 'Da—da' or

'Bow-wow', but, 'Let's all go back to my place!' That's
probably where you first met him. Swept along in a post-
party tide to his home where the drink and the chatter
flowed freely and where you began to wonder what he'd
be like if you got him on his own. You're still wondering.
There is barely one hour in the twenty-four when he is
not surrounded by assorted buddies, good guys or
'associates', he's met at the racecourse, the pub or 'a little
club I know round the corner'. Fancy a quiet night in
alone together? You should be so lucky. He'll breeze
through the door, just when you've had a dreadful day
and you begin tearfully, '. . . and another thing, Charlie,
the drains are blocked . . .' and you suddenly realize he's
not alone.

'I hope you don't mind,' a sheepish but merry face
appears behind Charlie's leather safari jacket, 'only Charlie
said it would be all right'.

'Of course she doesn't mind!' Charlie booms, slapping
you painfully on the buttock. 'Do you darling? I said you'd
never forgive me if I didn't bring Gerry back for dinner,
would you?'

He never stands still long enough for you to hit him.
Ducking and weaving, greeting and smiling, everyone
loves Charlie and he knows all their names. If you do put
your foot down and insist he phones you if he's bringing
someone home for a meal, it's always when he's on his
way.

'I've got Madge and Derek with me! Isn't that a surprise?
We haven't seen them since Gold Cup day. I said they'd
have to come back and say hello. We can rustle up
something, can't we?' He's put the phone down before
you can scream, 'What can I do with a tin of anchovies
and a can of spaghetti hoops not to mention that I've got
to keep this perm solution on for another ten minutes or

I'll look like Louis the Fourteenth!'

You can always find Champagne Charlie at the bar in the local pub drinking 'shorts', telling stories and recounting long and desperately boring jokes with punch-lines like 'Don't ask me, I'm a pragmatist!' which everybody laughs at because, as Charlie knows, they don't want to admit that maybe they don't find it funny because they don't understand it.

Champagne Charlie can always get tickets for anything you want — Ascot, Henley, Wimbledon, the Cup Final. 'I know a little man at the gate,' he says, tapping his nose. 'Just have to slip him a few quid for a drink.' Charlie carries large amounts of cash at all times and he's always buying drinks. Whatever your joint financial situation, you'll never see Charlie tighten his belt, cut-down on his off-licence order or lower his voice. It's his partner who has to cut down, of course, watch the housekeeping, while Charlie is still a regular at the golf club and the local watering holes and being as reckless as ever. 'I say that calls for a drink!' he'll announce, even if you've just pawned your engagement ring to pay the milkman.

It's not easy being a sidekick of Champagne Charlie. You'll be surrounded by people who seem to know him better than you do and you'll quickly discover that sensitivity is not Charlie's strong point. 'Great girl, my wife,' is a typical Champagne Charlie line, followed by a wink in your direction and then a numbing announcement, 'Did you know her thighs are different sizes?' The assembled roisterers, caught with g-and-t's teetering towards their lips, find their eyes inevitably drawn to the crimplene-clad limbs of Charlie's concubine and she is, once more, stunned speechless by the crassness of his conversation.

Treatment

This may be kill or cure but one thing guaranteed to burst Champagne Charlie's bubbles is embarrassment. One multi-humiliated bride of CC, peeved at having to answer her front door eleven times to people she'd never allow to check the oil on her car but who Charlie had dragged back from the bookies after 'a bit of luck on the 3.30' decided she'd had enough.

Fighting her way through the heaving throng, dipping into her vodka and stubbing cigarettes out on her knick-knacks on the sideboard, she turned down the stereo, took a deep breath and addressed Champagne Charlie in ship-launching tones, 'Darling! The bailiffs are here!'

Mummy's Little Soldier

The first thing you should give Mummy's Little Soldier is not your body or monogrammed golf balls, but a drying-up cloth, just to check. Mummy's Little Soldier hasn't seen one at close quarters before. He will assume it is a cravat and knot it round his neck before going back

BEEFBURGERS

to the cartoon section in the newspaper. Yup, you've got one, all right.

MLS didn't leave home until he was 27 — and then it was to get married. Would you leave home if you had all your washing and ironing done, your bed made, a hot meal every day and breakfast in bed on a tray? My God, his mother's got a lot to answer for! She's waited on him hand and hip all her life. He's never been allowed to iron a shirt, cook a meal, rinse round a bath. His mother believes men should have bigger helpings, the comfiest chair and the choice of TV channel.

Try not to get involved with Mummy's Little Soldier. He is so impossible, he may drive you to violence. He has another alias, he is sometimes known as Completely Useless, or CU. His Scottish cousin is, naturally, known as CU Jimmy.

Mummy's Little Soldier doesn't have bedroom eyes so much as nursery eyes. That little boy lost look was probably the first thing you found attractive.

MLS carries a briefcase that looks like a satchel. He wears hand-knitted jumpers and peels his apple before eating it. He usually has a beard because he's completely useless at shaving and his face ends up covered with more bits of torn paper than a betting shop floor.

Was it on the youth club camping weekend or in the accounts office that MLS first appeared, trailing a cuff? 'My button's come off,' he sighed. If your response is 'Tough bananas', you may live to find a possible man. If, on the other hand, you sigh 'Give it here. I've got my portable sewing kit handy' you will find yourself not so much in love, as in service. You've got to take a firm hand with him because, unlike many other impossible men, he genuinely doesn't know how to iron or cook a meal. This means you will have to teach him. It's no good saying 'My

Gerald's completely useless,' and laughing about it. Not
only is that defeatist, but it is not true either: he is merely
untrained. If you do not train him you will end up getting
so cross that you will crown him with the iron before
many months have passed. 'Have I got any clean shirts?'
he bleats, brightly. 'Yes, but you'll need to iron one,'
should be your response. What you have to remember is
that at the back of the MLS brain is the firm belief that, if
he takes long enough about it, you will take over. Don't,
under *any* circumstances!

It doesn't matter if it takes him 'til Thursday fortnight to
iron the damn shirt, let him do it himself. You have years
of maternal damage to undo. He will not become Jeeves
overnight.

'Do you have to grill both sides of a beefburger?' comes
the plaintive cry. You thought you'd start him on
something simple, so you have your feet up in front of
the news while odd bangs and acrid smells issue from
your new ceramic hob. Every fibre in your body is forcing
you to storm into the kitchen and take over. *Don't!*

Even if he starts crying, even if there are flames, or it's
disgusting. Eat it, enjoy it and suggest he does it again.
Invite his mother round next time. She'll sit with pursed
lips on the edge of her seat, desperate to take over from
her Little Soldier while he's doing 'women's work'.

'Naturally, Gerald and I share the chores. He insists on
doing his share,' you tell her, and kick him 'til he smiles in
agreement.

If he looks resentful and starts smacking the door frame
and saying Mummy never made him clean his shoes, tell
him that if he wants this relationship to work, he has to
pull his weight with the wok.

Treatment

It's all one big treatment with Mummy's Little Soldier.
Look for the warning signs. Stop yourself filling the
freezer every time you go to stay with your mother
overnight. It could take years, you'll have to put up
with burnt shirts and uncooked mince. Personally, I'm
not sure it's worth the effort.

Narcissus

Narcissus is so over-developed, they call him Milton Keynes. He's into body-awareness (mostly his) and he'll push you out of the way to get to a mirror. Naturally, he's a member of a health-club and he spends

so much time there, he contributes to the gas bill. His exercise gear is those soppy, skin-tight dungarees with braces. He looks like a 10-stone baby. At work, he favours waistcoats which emphasise the curve of his shoulders.

Narcissus is Californian by instinct, though not often by birth. If he wasn't going to live forever, he'd plan to die looking 21. He's Cliff Richard with biceps and can often be found entering the Eurovision Song Contest. He walks like a constipated sailor, on account of his having thighs like tree stumps.

Nothing will persuade Narcissus that most women don't want a man with a body like a sack of King Edwards and much prefer wilting poets with sensitive cheekbones. You can't win with Narcissus. His brains are in his biceps and he's got a gadget to monitor every organ in his body. Yes, *every* organ. He takes his blood pressure and pulse rates after he's honoured you with the programmed passion of his pneumatic physique. Go back to his place and there's so much gym gear lying around that you're likely to break a leg falling over his exercise bike.

His flat is full of honey muesli, photographs of himself, glistening like a Christmas turkey and barrels of vitamins, because he's a raging hypochondriac, of course.

If you're going out together for the evening, don't even think of hailing a cab. 'The restaurant's only up the road and it's a beautiful night,' he'll beam, blinding you with his radiator teeth and vaulting the front gate. 'Up the road' means the next county and you've worn your temper *and* your satin pumps to a frazzle by the time the bistro appears on the horizon.

His ideal woman is a bleached blonde in a leotard with an 'A' level in self-absorption. If you don't take as much care of your body as he does, he'll ask you to walk ten paces behind him or meet him *inside* the cinema. When he squeezes your thigh, he's checking for signs of cellulite, not awakened ardour.

He's often got a part-time job as a Tarzan-ogram and his approach to picking up girls is just that — pick them up! If he swings you over his shoulder and you sigh, 'My! Aren't you a big boy?' you will preen happily ever after with a wall-to-wall mirror. If, however, you respond 'Put me down, you huge fool!' keep on searching for that wilting poet.

A warning sign that you've picked a Narcissus is that you met him when he was running — for a train, for a bus or, worse, just for the hell of it. *Real men don't run.* Real men consider running is just walking hysterically.

Going out with Narcissus is like going out with Jane Fonda — without the laughs.

Treatment

There isn't any that will work. He's so busy treating himself with sunlamps, mineral supplements and body lotions that he'll hardly notice any additional interference from you.

Apart from plastering photos of Woody Allen all over your bedroom and sighing every time Columbo appears on television, your only hope is that one day he'll bend over too far at the local swimming baths, admiring his own reflection — and drown. Moist by his own façade!

The Entertainer

According to The Entertainer, only an accident of birth
prevented him from becoming, depending on his
age, the Tom Jones, Sting or Michael Jackson of his
generation.

'I can do better than that,' he'll claim, while watching

Top of the Pops or the *Des O'Connor Show*. The
Entertainer will sing not only in the bath but also in the
carwash.

He only has to hear the opening chords of *Please
Release Me* and he's off. In a key as yet unknown to the
musical theorists (E flat aborted), he gets the words
wrong, as well as the tune. It would be unfair, as well as
inaccurate, to describe the Entertainer as *just* a singer. He
may also be known as the man who can whistle *The
Flight of the Bumble Bee* (and frequently does) or, in
circumstances where singing, even by his almost non-
existent standards might be deemed inappropriate —
funerals or crowded trains — he will hum tunelessly and
relentlessly.

If he was born after the war, he will probably be a
guitarist. If you are visiting friends together, he will
discover a guitar lurking, even if your hosts have locked it
in the attic out of sight and, after two hours tuning, he will
launch into the inevitable *House Of The Rising Sun* with
a wail like a kicked chihuahua.

The Entertainer may not just be untalented in a
particular area. He is most likely to be an all round room-
clearer and when two or three are gathered together. He
will cause them to move swiftly apart as he delivers a
string of smutty and/or unfunny jokes, or reaches idly
towards the cutlery and begins playing the spoons and
tap-dancing. As long as he can lay his hands on a comb
and a piece of tissue paper (not difficult, as he keeps
them in his pocket), he'll always be ready with a
spontaneous concert. Unfortunately. 'That Bill, he is a
one!' some people say, not quite enlarging on what kind
of 'a one' Bill is.

He is much in demand at gatherings of the tone deaf
and the seriously drunk and is convinced that if only he'd

got in to see 'Bob', opportunity would have knocked for him years ago.

It is his partner, of course, who suffers most. Condemned to spend her life shouting over the chorus of *Send In The Clowns*, or waiting til he pauses for the instrumental break in *You Are The Sunshine Of My Life*, before she can tell him the house is on fire or that she's gone into labour, she's a martyr to music. Of a kind. There she'll be, at the tail end of a family wedding, surrounded by soggy confetti and skidded trifle, leaning on a pillar and looking at her watch while her starstruck half is up on the stage. He unclips his elasticated bow-tie, unbuttons his waistcoat, seconds before a button twangs off and ricochets off the bride's tiara, grabs the microphone with a chubby, be-ringed hand and adopts an expression which suggests a twisted knicker leg rather than a man in the grip of fiery passion. 'Feeeelings-ah . . .' he groans, eyes closed, identity bracelet dangling over a frayed cuff, 'Feelings like ah never left yeewwww . . .'

Treatment

It's impractical to spend your life wearing earplugs (you'd never hear the oven timer) but there are a couple of choices. You could buy him singing lessons for his birthday — but make sure you can run faster than him. Or you could start singing yourself. Do it very loudly and very often and during the football results. There is a faint chance that he might discover how irritating it is — but I wouldn't hold your breath.

The Perfect Father

You'll see the Perfect Father in the supermarket — pushing *two* trolleys, 'because Tristram and Isolde wanted a seat each'. He talks to the toddlers as if they are adults. 'Now, shall we have the cannelloni or the lasagne. What do you think?'

When he and his wife are out together, it is the PF who drones on endlessly about Tristram's little sayings and Isolde's distinction in her ballet exam. Before they were born, he read all the books, went to all the classes and, of course, he was there at the birth, reading Byron to her and having a life-enhancing experience.

He always asks other fathers if they watched their children being born. Those who answer that they had their children 'in the pub', he labels as unsuitable companions and won't let his children go to tea with theirs. He always reasons with his children. 'Now, why did you feel you had to drown the cat?' and *never* wallops them.

If his wife shows any signs of unseemly behaviour or bad language in front of them, the PF reacts like a teetotal mother-in-law at a stag party.

Nothing brings as much joy to the PF's heart as the jab of tiny knees in the groin at dawn and a golden head appearing under the duvet with the lisping request 'Read me a story, Daddy.' He is so seriously paternal that his wife often ends up being jealous of her own children. Warning signs of the dormant PF before children arrive are over-solicitous concern for your welfare. 'You'll need a coat. It's cold out.' 'You know I don't like you to drive after dark' or 'Sit down, I'll make you a nice cup of cocoa.' The kind of thing most women only hear once in a lifetime.

What the PF needs is something helpless, dependent and, above all, nice to look after. That's why he's absolutely useless when his children become snarling, stubborn, normal teenagers. Many wives who find the strain of being married to the PF is driving them up the wall, say they daren't leave him because 'being separated from his children would destroy him'. Rubbish! he'd go off and open an animal rescue centre. Never tell the wife of a

PF how lucky she is that her husband is so helpful and such a wonderful father to her children. She may kill you.

Treatment

Perfect harmony will result if you can revert to child-like behaviour yourself and let him look after you. Have a sulk, suck your thumb and be found in a corner cuddling teddy and trying to tie your shoelaces.

This may not be the answer to your problems but it will give your children some wonderful material for their autobiographies.

The Unromantic Type

The Unromantic Type's idea of foreplay is to shout 'Hello, dear, I'm home!' He'll only say 'I love you' if you ask him first — and then it's preceded by 'What's the matter? Is it *that* time of the month again?' Suggest you'd like to go out for dinner together and he'll invite

Brian and Sandra as well 'for a bit of company'. Prepare
an intimate candlelit dinner for two at home and he'll
come in, switch on the fluorescent tube and say 'Bit dark
in here. You got a migraine?' On Valentine's Day, you will
be bent double as you dole out his muesli, because you
have a giant card stuffed under your housecoat. It reads
'After all these years, you still bring me to my knees'. This
will shortly be true unless you donate it, swiftly, to your
true love. Unfortunately, you have not sensed a reciprocal
crackle beneath his towelling bathrobe. As the minutes
pass, and he turns to the sports page, you thwack him
over the head with the flower-strewn missive and follow
that with the news that he obviously doesn't love you or
he'd know what day it was. 'I'm just not the romantic type,'
he claims. This is not true. Everybody is the romantic
type, if they are properly trained.

Living with the Unromantic Type means wearing
placards around the house for weeks before your birthday.
He will still, however, forget and you will be forced to
raise your voice in an unseemly display of distress,
whereupon he will nip down the corner shop, return with
a Terry's chocolate orange, a bunch of elderly Michaelmas
daisies and a terribly pleased expression. He will not
understand your wail of 'It's not the same . . .!'

The partners of Unromantic Types are used to receiving
saucepans and oven-to-tableware as presents. They don't
like it, but they are used to it. During the early years of
togetherness, the wife of the UT, keen to appear good-
humoured, expresses joy and surprise as she unwraps a
set of dusters or a replacement head for her Squeegee
mop on her birthday. After all, she'd married him for his
sense of humour. Partly.

Now that the years have passed, so has her sense of
humour. 'I don't want a damn egg poacher for a present!'

she will cry, crowning him with it till his eyeballs revolve.
But he will not get the message. 'But you need one!' he
will respond, quite unable to see why a trip for two on the
Trans-Siberian Express or a peach peignoir with a string of
graded pearls might have gone down a bit better.

The UT is emotionally constipated. His partner
discovered this, if she was in any doubt, shortly after the
birth of her first child, when he came to visit her, shook
her hand and brought in a broken kettle to fix, to pass the
time. 'If I were his mistress,' the partner of the UT will
often yell with frustration at anyone handy 'would he
shower me with an adjustable ironing board and a wok?'
The answer is yes, because he does.

When courting, it is easy to fool yourself into believing
that the UT's lack of sensitivity is really an aloof strength
and strangely alluring. When you discover that behind
every strong, silent type is an awful lot of quiet, you've
only himself to blame. But just when you're about to give
up on him, he'll turn up with a bunch of yellow roses (the
red ones are too expensive).

This happens once every five years, on average. And
only after a helluva row.

Treatment

Risky, If you're strong, try drying up on the romantic
side yourself. Be distant, undemonstrative, self-
contained. One of two things will happen: either he
will realize something's different, wonder if you're
going off him and nip down the garden centre for a
concilitory potted hyacinth. Or he won't notice.

I'd put my money on the latter.

Myopic Man

If you are involved with Myopic Man, you often wonder what he sees in you. Does he, in fact, see anything? 'How do I look?' is the question most frequently directed at MM. 'Fine,' in his most effusive answer. If you've spent an hour at the beauty parlour, a

morning having your highlights done and bent your Access card on a backless halter-neck, 'fine' is simply not enough. Spend a fortune on a emerald green silk basque and twirl around in front of him and he'll ask you if you've seen his mole-wrench.

'Notice anything different about me?' is a desperate but unwise question to throw at the MM 'Yes, You've plucked your eyebrows at last!' was the response from one MM whose partner had just returned from a bust enlargement operation.

Sometimes, companions of MM's have to wait as long as the second Martini before having to tell him, 'This is a new dress, actually.' 'Yes, I noticed.'

'Well, do you like it?'

'It's very nice.'

'Why didn't you say anything?'

'I was just going to. You didn't give me a chance.'

How long is 'a chance'? Is 'a chance' halfway through the main course or is 'a chance' all the way from the avocado to the Tia Maria?

If your partner is Myopic Man, it is a deeply unrewarding and, indeed, humiliating experience to smother yourself with jojoba oil and slide into bed wearing nothing but a sensuous smile and a bit of satin that looks like a cat's cradle.

Many minutes will tick by while your expression of wicked expectation changes to thrumming frustration. Then, suddenly, his head will rise from the depths of *The Which Book of Home Improvements* and he will lean across your quivering body. You sigh in anticipation. A puzzled frown crosses his face and he delivers himself of a gem from Myopic Man's Book of Passionkillers:

'Are the Rennies on your side?'

Treatment

Take him for an *eye* test. You never know, he might be myopic. Stand around in a frock with a torn hem and a gravy stain on the chest. Ask him how you look. If he still says 'fine', leave him. He should have seen it coming.

NIGHTSHIFT

By Pete McKenna

S.T. Publishing
Street Literature At Its Very Best

To Ged Grennell, thanks for being there.

Nightshift (pbk)

© Pete McKenna, 1996

ISBN 1 898927 40 5

Published by S.T. Publishing, Scotland.

Printed by Progressive Printing, England.

Cover photo by Arthur Donaldson.

S.T. Publishing
P.O. Box 12, Lockerbie, Dumfriesshire. DG11 3BW. UK.

NIGHTSHIFT

By Pete McKenna

**Personal Recollections Of
Growing Up In And Around
The Casino Soul Club,
Empress Hall, Wigan
Sept. 1973 to Dec. 1981**

*Life is just one precious minute baby
Open up your arms and see it baby
Give yourself a better chance
Because time will pass you by.*

Pete McKenna spent a sizeable amount of his early years doing the all nighters at Wigan Casino between 1974 and 1981, where he over indulged in a nocturnal lifestyle of travelling, northern soul, great friendship and amphetamine abuse. After the Casino closed down, he travelled up and down the country working as a general building contractor. In 1991 recession forced redundancy on him and he immediately decided on a change of career.

He began writing in earnest two days after receiving notice of redundancy while residing in Brighton. A town he regards as his true home because of its history, style, pace of life and the change it brought about in him. *Nightshift* is his first book, and he has since completed two others. · *The Shower Room* which looks at the Holocaust in an alternative, but in no way revisionist light, and *An Eye For An Eye,* a modern day tale of murder and retribution most brutal, set on the south east coast of England, and a story that was inspired by an assortment of weird and wonderful people he has come into contact with over the last ten years.

His longstanding interest in crime and the law has led him to study for an LLB and is about to enter his third year as a student at The University Of Central Lancashire in Preston. He hopes to go on to study for a place at the Bar, or alternatively, study the area of Criminology. In between legal studies, further writing projects are already taking shape, one of which is about the shady lucrative world of advertising space and the dubious exploits of a couple of the local wide boys.

Apart from writing, his other interests are music, film, Indian and Thai food, good friends, anything made to measure, architecture, antiques, low life, no hopers, sleaze, and anything that has the ability to take his imagination away from the omnipresent cloud of cautious mediocrity that has enveloped the country for what seems like an eternity.

Long term ambitions? To maintain good friendships. Contentment. Success at either law or writing, and to own a Bristol 409. That would be nice.

Foreword

NORTHERN SOUL has become part of a never ending list of youth cults this country has produced. Its roots stretch from London and the 1950s jazz modernists scene, to today's rave scene culture.

The mods are the true grandparents of this now nationwide movement. A love of the "live now" ethic of drugs, mobility, fashion and popular culture that the 1960s and 1970s so expressed. Even the hippie excess of Woodstock et al could not break its spirit.

By 1969 the London scene had moved towards a funk rock psychedelia axis, but things were proving to be more resistant in the UK's industrial heartlands. The North and Midlands were host to a continuing burgeoning scene of mod like music lovers of Sixties style music and fashions, all helped by the London working class revolt of the mod offshoot culture known as skinhead.

Here lay the roots of the early Seventies original northern soul scene. *Blues And Soul* magazine's legendary soul writer, Dave Godin, is acknowledged with coining the phrase northern soul. Dave, a bearded academic type, understood the scene totally. He also understood the fanatical desire to musically rekindle the Sixties vibe in the Seventies, and venues like Manchester's Twisted Wheel really epitomised the scene as it stood in 1970.

Between 1970 and 1974, the scene was at its dizziest heights. Clubs like Stoke's Golden Torch, Blackpool's Mecca Highland Room, Bolton's Va Va's, and Wolverhampton's Catacombs, stood out as clubs catering for soul dance lovers who wanted mid-tempo and moody, or uptempo and stomping, sounds.

However, like all musical movements in this country, a peak was reached in 1974, when national media and rock music magazines picked up on the northern soul phenomenon of all night dancing, incredible stamina, drug abuse and an obsession with rarer and rarer records to play. Pop chart entries for some of the old records, which were now being reissued, compounded the problems and caused a crossroads-like split in the scene.

Most of the new blend of fans who made Wigan Casino their epicentre, following its infamous publicity in 1974, lacked the musical education of the older followers. They preferred more obvious ditties and overplayed oldies initially. However, in time, they recreated a new look northern scene for the 1980s and even the 1990s, which in retrospect helped the scene continue to mutate and develop into the legendary scene it is today in 1995. Original Wigan Casino DJ, Richard Searling, via his weekly Soul Sauce JFM Radio show, can now pull over 800 supporters to his Blackburn based northern soul revival sessions.

But what of the other northern soul fans who disliked the initial 1974 media spotlight? Well, people like myself found faith in the modernist creed of moving forward to remain "hip". We discovered Seventies soul and funk. Shared the early rave scene of house and New York dance music. Embraced aspects of the punk "do it yourself" ethic. Enjoyed the jazz funk scene and its counterparts, rare groove and now acid jazz.

However, we still maintained a deep love for the original scene created by DJs like Ian Levine (who helped break Take That as a recent pop phenomenon), Colin Curtis, Richard Searling and countless others. Today the scene has embraced many influences and the new wave of DJs coming through continue to mine that mid-soul axis, but in their own disparate ways.

When you read my old mate Pete's book, you will feel that vibe. That pull towards the epicentre of lovers of music in general, be it in 1995 rave, indie rock or hip-hop. However in our case, it is soul and its offshoots that keep us reading this honest and accurate account of a heady, pre-Thatcher Tory society still vibing out on that Sixties kick.

Things of course, will never be the same, but as long as people keep rediscovering our recent musical past, then the future of music in this country is assured in so many ways. At the end of this book is a list of 50 soul cuts that covers the wide range of northern soul. Many of them are available on the Kent, Goldmine and Charly CD compilations, so seek them out and enjoy!!!!

Keep the faith and respect.

Pete Haigh, 1995.

7

Introduction

I t all began back in the Blackpool of the early Seventies. An excuse for a town then, and even worse now, but at least in those days it was much closer to the object it purports to be. A bright and breezy seaside resort built to entertain the masses. Their very own Nirvana. A place where they could come and take their heads off for a couple of weeks, and attempt to pursue their idea of enjoyment. Then it had something more to offer beyond the candyfloss, hedgehog sandwiches, and big dippers.

It had a youth scene, alive and quite diverse for a town where diversity doesn't survive too well. And in amongst that diversity were the Okeh scooter crew. A cool bunch of local heads who oozed style, charisma and attitude in a place that had none. Dress code ranging from casual through to ultra smart. Mode of transport, only one way to go. Scooters. Lambrettas and Vespas, whose owners lavished unlimited amounts of love and attention on them to get them looking the absolute business. And didn't they look the business.

Tastes in music? Anything from ska and reggae to soul. You know the stuff. Stax. Atlantic and Tamla Motown. Excellent music, but at the top end of the mainly black soul commercial market and readily available to the masses. And then there was this other soul music that had been around since the Sixties. Uncommercial. Rarer and bursting with a rawness, an energy and a driving beat that just took you to another place. Northern soul, so called because of its popularity in the clubs and discos of northern England.

To many of us, northern soul was it. The only sound to listen to. And surprisingly enough, we didn't have to travel that far to find it because Blackpool itself was as good a place as any for northern at the time. South Shore Casino did an excellent Friday soul night with Baz Stanton behind the decks. The Peacock Room ditto. But the place to be if you wanted quality sounds with an atmosphere to match was The Highland Room, perched high in the Mecca complex on Central Drive.

For its size, the Highland Room was the tops. It had all the northern soul scene ingredients. Brilliant sounds. Brilliant people, packed together and getting on with it. Brilliant atmosphere and a prevalent gear scene too. Speed. Sulphate. Bombers, green and clears, Dexedrine or dexy's. Everything was available if speed was your thing. A couple of bombers down your neck and you'd be flying until the early hours, guaranteed. Yeah, the northern scene was alive and kicking there, and people would turn up from all over the country to sample the flavour of the Highland Room.

Meanwhile, we kept hearing the buzz about an old ballroom in Wigan doing the business. All nighters and spinning the best northern soul around. Membership only too, and growing by the day. Went by the name of the Casino Soul Club and it all sounded too much from the accounts we were getting from mates who'd done an all nighter there.

We decided to give it a go. Sent off for membership and in a week or so, it popped through the letter box and that was that. In no time at all we were in the queue outside this run down red brick ballroom waiting to go in and see what it was all about. Wondering what we'd experience once we were inside the place. That was back in March, 1974. Our first all nighter at Wigan Casino Soul Club. The venue that eventually rose to become the headquarters of the northern scene, and the place that kept us going back and back and back for the better part of six years before it all ended one night in December 1981, leaving us to adjust and return to a life of what's laughingly called normality.

The nine to five, five days a week job, then we'd put on our weekend heads and stand in overcrowded mock Tudor pubs, dressed to the nines. Chatting up future girlfriends and (for some of us) wives, as we swallowed pint after pint of lukewarm bitter, only to end up spewing the lot up in some dark back street, littered with used Tampax and dog shit, after the love of your life had blown you out. Then you attempted to stagger home all alone, to the safety of your pit and the coming week.

Why do all good things have to come to an end?

You Get Your Kicks . . .

Way back in 1972, if anyone had said to me that for the next seven years I would change all my social habits and totally immerse myself in an all night youth scene that operated out of some old run down ballroom that played nothing but this rare and raw music called northern soul, I would have told them as politely as possible to go and get their heads sorted out.

If they had also told me that in that seven year period, I would eat and snort my way through a skip full of speed, dance the equivalent of a round the world marathon, turn down the chance to fly fast jets for the RAF, watch the gradual and painful deterioration and death of a couple of my friends, and worse still, leave my old man to fend for himself after he had suffered a heart attack, and all because I had to get to this old ballroom bang on time in case I missed a second of what was going on in there, then I would have told them in no uncertain terms to fuck off. Just fuck right off and leave me well alone.

But it's weird how the unexpected turns out to be reality. All of this did happen, and much more too, before we walked down the staircase and into the bright morning sunlight for the last time, finally ending an often desperate, uncomfortable, but totally unforgettable relationship with the club that is now widely acknowledged to have been the capital of the UK soul scene of the Seventies, and the forerunner of the acid house-rave scene of more recent years. The club that came to be known as the Wigan Casino Soul Club, host of the now legendary all nighters.

It all began in the Blackpool of the early Seventies. Two decades before the widely grinning Mr Jeffrey Thompson, owner of the Pleasure Beach, held his breath and took his first ride on the Big One. The world's largest roller coaster called The Pepsi Max. The very same roller coaster that unexpectedly broke down somewhat prematurely after its official opening, from what is known in the trade as computer failure. Nice comfortable term is that. A very well disguised understatement that was meant to calm our nerves and entice us all back to the roller coaster with bags of confidence. Bet it felt like a million miles away from computer failure for the terrified passengers

11

trapped thirty feet up in the air, waiting to be rescued by the fire brigade on that fateful day.

Talk about the unexpected and all that!

So what was it like living in the Blackpool of the Seventies? The second most visited place after the Vatican would you believe. Well, on the menu was a staple diet of all the things that teenagers like to try out, if only the one time. Clothes, music, the opposite sex, football, alcohol, and drugs, although not necessarily in that order. You could get that diet anywhere in the country, but the big difference was that we had all the fantastic attractions that have made Blackpool the entertainment capital of the Western World, right at our very own fingertips to use and often abuse at will. What a lucky bunch of ungrateful bastards we were.

It was a lot more colourful a place to live in during those days too. More real somehow, if you could ever assimilate such a word as real with Blackpool. It seemed to be a galaxy away from the multi-million pound money-making giant it has turned into these days. The vibe has changed, but all the same attractions are still there. The world famous Blackpool Tower. The Pleasure Beach. The three Victorian piers you can still stroll up and down as you lick your 99 Woppa ice cream. Or you can hire a deck chair for the day and fall asleep while the sun slowly but surely bakes you from pale to a nice shade of lobster red, and leaves you in agony for the remainder of your stay in sunny old Blackpool.

The illuminations are still there, bigger, brighter and longer than they ever were. The entire length of the seven mile promenade is lit up by a million light bulbs every year towards the end of the holidaymaking season, with a thousand different characters to thrill you. From Fred Flintstone through to Luke Skywalker and Arnie. All lit up to bring your two weeks in Blackpool to a spectacular end. Take it a step further and see the lights from a Blackpool tram disguised as a rocket ship or a steamboat before you head home with your head crammed full of seaside memories.

But before you do go, try out the Golden Mile with its bingo halls, amusement arcades and hamburger stalls that have been there almost as long as the town itself. It's not as golden as the name would suggest, but it is an area of the town that has retained some spirit of what a seaside resort used to be like. That's if you can discount the hedgehog sandwiches. And there are the golden beaches and the blue sea, or so we are led to believe. At least that's how they are portrayed on the

12

millions of postcards on sale in the town. If you wanted a more realistic view of the state of the Blackpool coastline, then the environmentalists could provide you with one. It ain't Copacabana by any stretch of the imagination and it's a place that locals don't go near. But if you fancy taking your chances on a beach booby trapped with broken bottles, and enjoy swimming in a sea infested with shit and sanitary waste, then get your trunks on and go for it.

A few years ago, Greenpeace came to town to conduct some tests of the surrounding coastline and after completing them, announced that it was unsafe to swim in the very same water that earned Blackpool millions. The results could have proved disastrous for the town so something had to be done to prove otherwise, and one brave spirited Tory leader of the community was the man to do it. He was going to prove that all the tests carried out were bullshit, and a product of the loony left element that was gradually creeping into our society. But how was this pinstripe suited stalwart going to do this? By drinking a pint of good old Blackpool sea water. That's how.

So amidst a flurry of activity from the press, members of the council and an army of hard pressed irate landladies, the Tory laughingly downed a pint of coastal brew and actually lived to tell the tale. Huge sighs of relief from all concerned followed, and calm was restored once again. Conclusive proof that Blackpool sea water was indeed safe to swim in. The effluent, the excreta, the strange brown froth and the tampons were still there, but it was safe to drink so that was that.

Since it began its meteoric rise to number one in the seaside resort top ten, it has remained a working class resort, no matter how much it strives to break away from the rolled up shirt sleeves and flat cap image. Nowadays of course it's all beer bellies poking out from baggy shell suits, and trainers the size of diving boots. But you will still find readily available masses of cheap accommodation, cheap food and a friendly reassuring smile from the symbol that has come to epitomise the town over the years. The waving landlady standing on the red glossed stone steps of her boarding house, welcoming you to a world of woodchip and early morning fry ups. Had too much to drink the night before and you can't make it down for breakfast for fear of spewing up all over your corn flakes? No sweat, because there are a thousand cafes eager to fill you up with bacon, eggs, sausages, tomatoes, fried bread and a steaming mug of hot tea at any time of the day. With that little lot inside you, your cholesterol levels will be well and truly topped up for the day, and you will be up and running for another ten pints of Stella. Lovely!

If you're a person with slightly more discerning tastes, then you will be severely pissed off if you ever find yourself in Blackpool, thinking that perhaps it might offer some hidden charm. Forget it. There are no quaint hard to find antique shops down crowded narrow lanes. No continental style piazzas tucked away behind splendid Georgian facades where stylish people take their time over expresso coffees or chilled beer, reading or conversing on subjects a million miles away from tits in *The Sun* and Gazza's latest tearful outburst.

Sadly, you will find none of that but if your tastes are more down to earth and you are in search of good old fashioned fun, then it's the place for you. If you are a family man, then all the better because there are lots of things to get up to that will keep your offspring wide eyed and spellbound for hours on end. You will discover a wonderland of adventure bristling, with every conceivable attraction expected from what has become the mecca of entertainment, even on a wet day. There's a curious mix of the tried and tested, traditional and the high tech. From hot dogs, candy floss and fortune tellers to state of the art, albeit occasionally unreliable, white knuckle rides that will leave you breathless - though hopefully, only temporarily.

But to a lot of the locals with half a brain, Blackpool is a very different place to the one the tourist board incessantly strives to portray to the outside world. To them it is an unstoppable, predominantly concrete, Alcatraz. A maximum security fun palace devoid of any art or culture. A strange land where the Big Mac and fries reign supreme, and the locals play second fiddle to a vast tourist army of occupation.

Then one morning you walk down the street and into town and you sense something is wrong. Things aren't quite as they used to be. You can walk down the street in a straight line without bumping into a cast of thousands. They are all gone. All fucked off back to where they came from. All you find is deserted streets and boarded up cafes, the owners of which have cleared off to Spain for the winter. All of a sudden there are no people and it's weird. Like something out of the cult sci-fi movie, *The Omega Man*. And that's it until the next year. And just when you are getting used to all the space, the tourists are back in their thousands. Grockles we call them.

To be cool in Blackpool in the early Seventies, you could go one of several ways. You could do the coolest thing and get a place at university. Pack a suitcase and fuck right off out of the town.

14

Alternatively, you could drop out and join the hippies with their long hair, loons, Afghan coats, multi-coloured Doctor Who scarves, oil of patchouli and drugs. Get yourself down to the dole and sign on for the summer. Do the festival circuit and overdose on psychedelia. Come the winter, and do the pilgrimage to India or Thailand in search of the hidden truth behind the real meaning to life. Or maybe it was nothing more than a search for more mind-blowing drugs to trip out on. Yeah, maybe that was more like it.

There was a large mob of hippies in Blackpool then. Stoneheads we used to call them, but it was a term of affection really. They were an okay bunch. Used to use a large town centre pub called The Blue Room not far from the Art College where just about every Stonehead went to study. Enter The Blue Room just about any night of the week and they'd all be there. Huddled under their long hair and beards, and the thick Chernobyl-like cloud of dope that blanketed the pub permanently. All of them completely out of it and grooving away to *Smoke On The Water*, *Paranoid* or *Dark Side Of The Moon*. They took a lot of shit from the skinheads and the grockles. They just didn't understand them at all and so took the easy path when you come up against something you don't quite understand. Yeah, that's right. Kick the shit out of them. Far easier than actually getting to know them and what they think about life. It's still there today, The Blue Room. Full of a new generation with different faces and different attitudes, but the essential spirit that made it the number one alternative pub is still there. The hippies are still there and the drugs are still there. But the skins have all but disappeared these days, and the grocks stay well clear in case the Goths eat them alive.

Then there were the bikers and greasers with their long hair and beards, sleeveless denim jackets and leathers, hob nailed boots and filthy oil stained 501s. They took their look from their American counterparts, the Hell's Angels, and also a few of their habits too. There were two mobs in Blackpool to watch out for. The Fylde Coast Road Hogs and The Blood 22, and both were fucking mental when it came down to doing the business. It was like they hated just about everybody except their own kind. They had their own bikes, music and their own birds. And their own way of sorting out aggro when it came their way. Every so often we would have the run in with them. The occasional aggro. It would all be arranged weeks before the day so the cops were left in the dark. Meet up on some deserted car park. Twenty, maybe thirty a side and proceed to kick the fuck out of each other until the cops eventually arrived to call a halt to the fun. The greasers were tough brutal fuckers who would stop at nothing in a battle, but it didn't always go their way. Not all the time. But it was a fucking nightmare going in against them. Standing there shivering on a cold stony floored car park waiting for the off. And them with their hob nailed boots, lump hammers, knives and their favourite toy, the bike chain.

Get a few strokes from a heavy bike chain and you'd know about it. Didn't exactly give you confidence to stay and do the business, but there was no way out. Run away and you'd be branded a shithouse, and end up getting your head kicked in by your own mates. Yeah - your own mates. You couldn't win, and the old saying, "he who turns and runs away lives to fight another day", just went right out of the window. Talk about the joys of growing up.

The mods were making a massive comeback on the scene. Not only locally, but right across the country. The scooter riding much hated rivals of the greasers. Neo-offsprings of the original much sharper, mohair suited mods of the Sixties who successfully developed a hybrid culture of English tailoring and attitude with the finest Italian two wheeled engineering style. The same mods had battled with the greasers in quaint south coast sea side towns, culminating in the mass pitched battles down in Brighton. The very riots that were behind the inspiration for the film *Quadrophenia*, which starred Sting sporting a silver suit and a winning smile as he paid the fine imposed on him in court the way you would expect the leader of the mods to pay up. In cash.

A few of my mates already had their scooters, or chairs as we called them, so I decided to jump in and get one sorted out. Talk about easy. Applied for HP down at the then local Lambretta dealer who was doing a no questions asked roaring trade. I filled in the usual forms and after a five minute wait, the salesman told me that all was in order. I could take it away in a week's time.

"That's it?" I asked.

"Yeah - see you next week. Early Saturday morning," he replied.

Went down a week later and exchanged a firm handshake and a "good luck" for a set of keys to my new chair. A gleaming brand new bog standard Lambretta GP. After a brief lesson on how to ride it from the main man, I sat astride it, fired it up and roared off into the proverbial sunlight with my monthly repayment book flapping around in the top pocket of my old Levi's denim jacket. I was oblivious to

16

everything else on the road as I concentrated on travelling in a straight line.

A few weeks later, after several death defying escapes learning to ride it in a safe and proper manner, I set about the job of customising it. Jet black paintwork with chrome plated side panels and front bumper, and a rakishly angled backrest fixed to the back of the seat. Suddenly, AFR 539L looked the absolute bollocks of a chair and I was well pleased with the new look. Well pleased.

There was a large scooter mob in Blackpool in those days that ran under the name of the Okeh scooter crew. Took their name from a much respected northern soul record label, and each crew member sported a handmade shield on the back of his chair just to let Joe Public know who he was fucking dealing with. The shields were much sought after objects of desire, especially among the motorbike riding members of the local scene who tried their best to grab a few whenever we locked horns. But those shields. Well we'd sooner die than let some greasy long hair get his grimy fingers on them.

There remained an almost perpetual state of war between us and the greasers. No punches pulled and absolutely no prisoners taken, and often it went the whole way which meant a fucking good kicking and a hospital bed for a few days. They always had the edge on us because their bikes could outstrip our chairs easily, which meant they could catch us no problem. They'd draw up alongside us and try their best to kick us off the road while we fought back with lump hammers and chisels, and all this activity going on while we were steaming down the Queen's highway with other traffic everywhere.

One afternoon we were out on the road and it was perfect. The sun was out and the town was crammed with birds. We were out cruising around. Going easy on the throttle and zipping in and out of the traffic like a couple of wasps. All of a sudden it was scramble as a half dozen of the hairiest greasiest bastards that ever sat astride a motorbike appeared in the rear view mirrors. We opened up and weaved in and out of just about everything and everyone in an attempt to shake them off our tail and to avoid the obligatory good kicking, but it was hard work. We were only two handed that day so it was every man for himself as we split up and headed for home.

I hung on to see if my mate had made it home safely, but he didn't. The greasers caught him just outside his house. He ditched his chair and legged it to safety, as the greasers whooped it up over the fact that they had caught a scooter. Set about kicking it into a new shape and one that wasn't half as good as the original one. Worst of all though was the fact that he had only had his new respray a couple of days. The paint was barely dry and there he was. Forced to watch the temporary death of his chair from the safety of his front room. Pure agony, but as bad as it was, we knew there would be other time, when we would get our own back on the greasy twats.

We would meet up every Sunday like clockwork at the Okeh cafe. Yeah, we even had our own cafe. In name at least. Park the chairs up and grab some breakfast and a cup of coffee and sit back admiring all the chairs parked up in the sunlight. When everyone had been accounted for, we'd fire up the engines, slip into first gear and roar off en masse, leaving behind a peculiar blue cloud of two stroke exhaust smoke. Then it would be onto the promenade to soak up the vibes and check out anything that wore a skirt, while keeping one eye out for the greasers who used the promenade as much as we did.

We looked a wicked bunch as we cruised the streets in tight formation. The vibe was unbeatable. Bright sunlight, a packed promenade, a joint between your lips and the sound of a hundred tuned up Lambretta and Vespa engines pop-pop-popping away. No crash helmets either to cramp your style as you tore up the road with the wind in your hair and looked out to the world from a pair of chrome rimmed mirrored shades. All of us looking like a bunch of extras from *Quadrophenia*, only much cooler. One of the better memories of growing up in Blackpool.

The weekend runs were something else too, and the highlight of an otherwise boring week. We'd all get together and head off for distant lands, and clashes with the police and anybody else who wanted to have a go at us. Bank holidays were even wilder as seaside towns like Morecambe, Scarborough, Brighton and Margate were invaded for the duration of the holiday by masses of scooterists, out for fun and adventure. Fur trimmed parkas and chairs everywhere.

Aggro would kick off in pubs and clubs all over the town. Within hours of arriving, you would see welcoming signs going up proclaiming "no scooterists served in here". Police vans on every corner with fierce looking Alsatians growling and straining at the leash, and showing off their sharp nasty looking teeth in an attempt to keep us all in order. Hordes of blue helmets everywhere waiting to nick us as we got through bottles of off licence alcohol. If the pubs refused our custom, then the off licences certainly didn't, much to the annoyance of the local plod, but after all, business was business to some people, regardless of the consequences. But it would only be a matter of time before the cops would move in and attempt to sort us out.

Some of the towns we visited on a regular basis got so fucked off that they brought in emergency measures as if they were preparing for a wartime invasion. Roadblocks would be set up a few miles from town and once we had all been stopped, we would be escorted to large open camp sites, usually very muddy ones with no facilities.

The local plod would be on us all the time. When we made a move, there they would be, right on our tail in an attempt to monitor us. Their overly heavy presence would eventually wind us up that little bit too much and it would all kick off. Us against them. Trouble would flare up in sporadic bursts, followed by mass arrests and brutal kickings in the back of transit vans from cocky, stressed out police officers who seemed to really enjoy that part of the job. And there would be even more of this in store for us back in the privacy of the nick. And for those among us who really flipped out over the top and took it too far, you know serious assault on a plod, then they would be kept in for the weekend and brought before special courts on the Monday morning to face justice from the blue rinsed poker faced magistrates who handed out crippling fines to anyone who stood before them.

In the space of a weekend you would be virtually guaranteed a hangover, a run in with the local plod, trouble with the local greasers who never failed to turn up and have a go at the scooter army, and a night in the police cell. And on the way home you'd have the inevitable roadside breakdown when all you wanted to do was get home for some much needed rest.

Even usually good spirited local motorists would jump on the anti-scooter bandwagon and have a go. Anything to contribute to the downfall of these yobbos and all that. We'd be sat at traffic lights waiting for the green and up he would come. The squeaky-clean living, tweed-jacketed, bespectacled citizen, out for his weekend drive in his immaculate no miles on the clock Ford Granada, with the obligatory good little woman by his side, and two kids and a bored looking overweight Golden Labrador in the back.

Looks of disgust would be thrown at us, and they would be followed by derisory comments. You know the thing. "Bloody yobs. What you lot need is a dammed good thrashing and three years in the army and if I was twenty years younger, you would know about it!"

We'd shout back, the lights would change, and we'd roar off leaving him with a dented wing or minus a wing mirror. He'd still be in neutral, and cursing us all. But he got one thing out of it. Enough after dinner conversation about the decline of law and order and the alarming lack of moral standards to last the old git six months. And not forgetting the glorious day he stood firm like a rock against the hun-like degenerate scooter riding louts. A real fucking hero, if only at the dinner table.

And then you'd get the other breed of motorist. The one who puts his actions into words. The Mad Max "I will show these fucking bastards a thing or two, you see if I don't" type. Cocky and fiercely territorial, with Made In Britain etched into his heart. Solid working class. Apprenticeship this and apprenticeship that, with a healthy over respect for all things law and order. The kind of guy who knows his place in life, even though the nappy marks are still on him. Football fan, weightlifter, and good with his hands. The type of guy who can transform a wreck of a Ford Escort into a full spec fire-breathing Group One rally car replica in under a weekend, and still have time to have a night out on the beer with his mates, shag the arse off his adoring Barbie doll of a girlfriend, and keep the sun tan topped up, courtesy of the Costa Del sun bed.

There he would be, waiting at the lights, gnashing his teeth and flexing his pecs as he saw us approaching in his rear view mirror. Drumming angrily on the steering wheel, wondering why these mods, with their fucking stupid sunglasses and scooters, were allowed on the same road as his pride and joy. All it would take would be one look or a laugh from us that he assumed was directed at him, and that would be that. He'd be out of the car, shouting and pulling one of the chaps off his chair, and laying into him.

And I'm afraid that really would be that. The lads would dismount and proceed to kick the seven shades out of him, leaving him battered and bruised in the mini-skirted lap of his distraught Barbie doll who was left to wipe away the blood and Doc Marten prints from her once gorgeous sun tanned Lancelot. The fucking wanker.

We were (or so we thought) a cool looking bunch of bastards. The epitome of teenage cool and this was reflected in the way we all looked after our chairs. Each of us being fiercely proud of our own piece of Italian engineering. We showered them with devotion and went to extraordinary lengths to get them looking as individual as possible.

Intricate custom paint jobs teamed up with chrome plating. Some of the chaps went fully chrome and they really did look the business. A fully chromed chair with all the bolt-ons looked totally cool, but along with the top spot came a life long sentence of continually having to clean your pride and joy in an attempt to keep it free from the ravages of the salt-laden Blackpool air. Some of the chaps managed it to perfection, but others gave up the ghost and returned to the good old wash down and wax cellulose paint job. Easy life. Easy life!

Each week you could spend your wages on the vast array of tasty accessories available. Flyscreens, chrome crashbars, bumper bars, legshield tool boxes, whitewall tyres, spotlights, and backrests teamed up with low profile racing seats. Get that lot on your scooter and you would be numero uno for sure. Mechanically you could stretch out the humble Innocenti two stroke to its absolute life-risking limits. There were racing clutches and outsized carbs that took your power up to a decent limit. Your miles per gallon was cut, but what's money when you are in pursuit of power? You could fit oversize pistons and barrels that would take you out even further to well past the standard 200cc. Get even more power with a high performance tune up. Fit one of those big bore Ancillotti racing exhaust systems and you would own a chair that moved like lightning and sounded as sweet as any Kackle Wilson track. Orgasmic.

The cops always gave us an overdose of shit whenever we took to the road and one in particular really made us sweat. He made it his role in life to bust as many of us as possible and anyone else connected with the Okeh scooter crew. We christened him Ratface - and he really earned the name. The pleasure he got from booking any of us was clear to see in his face. You'd think he'd just had the fuck of a lifetime some days when he took you through a roadside check. He would lie in wait at a certain roundabout we all used on the way out of town. We'd never see him, but he was there. You could smell him in the air and then suddenly he would be on you, indicating for you to pull over and switch off.

His bike would be up on its stand and he'd slowly approach you wearing a wide grin of delight at the prospect of busting yet another specimen of shitty, scooter riding low life. The sort of bloke who would have gone down a storm in Nazi Germany or South Africa. Just the right type. He would take his time and go through all the script with you, item by item. Lights, brakes, exhaust, tyres, the lot. Then he would measure the distance your mirrors projected from your chair. There was a legal maximum distance they were allowed to protrude and if any exceeded the distance, then you were a goner for sure. He would order you to remove them due to them constituting a danger to other road users, and if he was feeling really mean, he'd confiscate them. If he'd had his leg over the night before, then he would feel slightly more lenient. If not, you would be a dozen mirrors down.

After initial visual tests, he would really get down to business and check out your legals. Your licence would be given a meticulous once over to see if you had passed the test that allowed you the luxury of not having to display those distinctly uncool L-plates. If you were a learner with no L-plates on show, he would have you for sure. And God help you if you were a provisional licence holder and happened to be carrying a passenger. You were really fucked and definitely down for a personal appearance in the magistrates court, which in turn meant plenty of sweating and sleepless nights waiting for the big day to come and go with the minimum of fuss.

To undergo a standard Ratface check was a bad scene. Pure Freddie Kruger stuff. To get through one with a clean sheet was a miracle. A few of the chaps managed it and they'd pull away laughing and throwing him a few fucks as they roared off. Understandable, but not a good move. Ratface never ever forgot a face. Especially one that gave him the vee sign after a road check.

For the majority of us, the end result of a Ratface pull would be an appearance in court, and a fine. All you had to do was look smart, wear a suit, be respectful and keep your big mouth shut and you'd be out of there before you could say Ratface. Well, nearly as quick. Not all the local plod did the business like he did, but that Ratface - man, he was in a league apart. A total loner.

And then last, but not least, Blackpool had its skinheads. Shaven headed, big booted members of an aggressive looking anti-social youth culture. They had spread in popularity throughout the length and breadth of the country during the early Seventies, after first going public in 1969 during the Rolling Stones free festival in Hyde Park. While the pouting Mick Jagger, dressed in a white dress, belted out his lyrics to a massive crowd, the skinheads clashed with the notoriously violent Hell's Angels under the hot London sun. The skinheads had arrived and they weren't going to go away.

The skinhead army grew at a phenomenal rate as thousands of teenagers adopted the look. They were everywhere, even on the bookshelves, with the movement being glamorised in a series of hard hitting violent paperbacks written by Richard Allen and published under The New English Library. They had titles like *Skinhead, Bovver Boys* and *Suedehead,* and featured the exploits of West Ham skinhead

22

leader, Joe Hawkins. A racist anti-Semitic thug. One marked flaw in Joe's thinking was the fact that both a Jewish kid and a coloured guy were in his vicious gang. Never did get the logic behind that one, Joe.

That aside, Joe and his gang were the creme de la creme of the football hooligan army who meted out a classless violence to all who happened to get in their way, intentionally or otherwise. Both on and off the terraces they ruled so brutally.

The books rapidly became popular and served as readily available style guides for all potential recruits who wanted the clothes Joe and his gang wore. Contained in the pages were the essential items that made up the skinhead uniform. An image that to this day remains one of the most striking of all the images youth cultures have developed. It was even glamorised on the big screen at the time in *A Clockwork Orange*, Stanley Kubrick's futuristic orgy of violence and mayhem.

Levi's denim jackets and jeans. Fred Perry sportshirts. Ben Sherman and Brutus shirts. Sta prest trousers. Two tone suits and crombie overcoats. And of course the item that above all others has come to symbolise the skinhead movement. The Doctor Marten Air Wair boot. The good old bovver boot. Everyone has either owned a pair of these boots or been on the receiving end of them.

The skins adopted the boot as their footwear, the symbol of a movement. At the same time, they did the company a massive big favour as, unbeknown to the skins, it was on the verge of financial collapse. But today the firm is a worldwide success and Martens are everywhere to be seen. A much recognised and coveted fashion accessory available in many mind-blowing colours and patterns from pink patent through to tartan and Prince of Wales check, and worn by men and women alike. They even do a pair of Martens with a "vegetarian" sole now for people who like their footwear animal free. Society has taken to the Marten in a big way. Schoolgirls, grungers, architects, punks, and new age travellers all know what it feels like to get into a pair of Martens and bounce down the street. Everybody should experience that feeling once in their life.

But before the fashion industry caught on to them, and more importantly accepted them, they were only available in two colours. Black and cherry red. And in those days, Doctor Martens were used for things other than walking up and down the catwalk. One of them was aggro, with skinheads from opposing towns meeting up every Saturday afternoon on the terraces of football grounds to kick the fuck out of one another. This is where the bovver boot came into its own. Worn with

Levi's jeans that were turned up to display the boots to their full menacing potential.

Everybody I knew nurtured their Martens with the care and attention usually only reserved for dying relatives or girlfriends. They sweated for hours applying layer after layer of Tuxan red polish on their prized possessions, bulling them up to a mirror-like shine that a guardsman would have been proud of. You could even go to the lengths of antiquing your boots by applying black polish to the creases, letting it soak into the leather and after a couple of weeks, there they were. A pair of antiqued stitch ups ready for the off. And just when you had got them looking perfect, Saturday afternoon would come around and you'd be off to the match where once again, they would end up scuffed and scratched and in need of further love and attention. Still, it gave you something to do between matches. It was like sex sometimes, polishing your Docs week in, week out. Exhausting, demanding and ritualistic if you know what I mean.

I remember to this day the first time I bought a pair of cherry reds. The old man had been giving me loads of grief because he didn't want me to get a pair, but I was having none of it. *Fuck it*, I thought. *I'm having a pair and that is that.* I caught the bus to a small village near Blackpool. The only place that stocked decent Martens. Handed the guy behind the counter the cash, and he gave me this big brown box containing a pair of the finest cherry reds, and a couple of tins of Tuxan red polish. Sat on the back seat upstairs all the way back with a hard on. Every now and then I'd open the box and take a deep smell of the new leather. Got them home. Tried them on in front of the mirror. A perfect fit and spent the rest of the night slowly polishing them - even though they didn't need it. And listening to the *Skinhead Moonstomp* album, which incidentally featured Blackpool skins on the front cover. God I looked after those Martens. I had it real bad. What was the song? Oh, yeah . . .

> *"I want all you skinheads to get up on your feet.*
> *Put your braces on your jeans and your boots on your feet.*
> *And gimme some of that old moonstomping!"*

Then after the skins came the boneheads and suedeheads. The boneheads were a breed apart. I mean like they were really off it with their totally shaven heads that made them appear more aggressive than the skins. A number one crop was bad enough, but when you saw a mob of boneheads approaching you, you would think twice about staying on the same side of the road as them. They looked evil and dangerous beyond belief. And the suedeheads too. Skinhead offsprings who favoured the skinhead lifestyle and image without the anti-social haircut. In Blackpool in the early Seventies, there was a large mob of suedeheads who made it their number one priority to be the epitome of teenage cool.

As a teenager in Seventies Blackpool, it was crucial to get yourself an edge. It just had to be done because without it, you were nowhere. It was a fashion conscious town and the shops were packed with all the right on gear. Levi's, Ben Shermans, Brutus, Slazenger jumpers, Royals and loafers, crombies and sheepskins.

With all those you'd have the look, but not the edge. For the edge you had to look elsewhere, out of town. And there was only one elsewhere. Manchester. The once a month shopping expedition would get you the edge, ahead of the rest of the crowd. If only for a month or so, but that month meant everything.

You would arrive early morning in the precinct in the town centre. Grab some early breakfast and have a mooch about the boutiques, checking out the clothes. Try a few things on and if they looked right, you'd buy them and get out of there before the black gangs arrived looking for guys like us to have over. Mug us and nick all our new gear. There were loads of them, hanging around outside the shops, trying to get you to have a fight or to intimidate you into handing over your shopping or cash. That's why we always made the trip early to avoid the aggro with them.

We mixed up casual style with smart style to fit the mood we were in at any given time. Denims, Fred Perry's and Doc Martens for the aggro and the scooters. Suits, blazers, made to measure trousers, all leather brogues or smoothcaps for smarter occasions. Timpson shoes did a splendid shoe called the Royal. All leather and they weighed a ton, but great value for money and did they last. They sure did.

For suits you couldn't go wrong if you stepped into Jackson's, the tailor. A nationwide chain of tailors who made good class suits in a wide variety of styles and as an added bonus, all of them available on the never never. You would be measured up, pay a small deposit, and in under a month, you'd be the proud owner of a hand-tailored two piece suit. Made to measure blazers were well popular and extremely cool looking with a pair of their tailored trousers, complete with sewn in creases. And let's not forget the famous Jackson's silk lined, fly fronted made to measure crombie, the business of an overcoat and infinitely superior to the mass produced cheaper versions that Stone-Dri used to pump out. Just wearing a Jackson crombie made you feel like a king.

If you could afford to treat yourself to a little luxury, you could go for the three-quarter length sheepskin coat. Very expensive, but a much needed accessory, especially among the scooter riding fraternity. The Okeh crew rode their chairs all year round. Not just in the summer months under a blazing hot sun, but in the bonechilling winter when the cold cramped you up from the neck down after an hour's drive. Looking good then took a back seat to keeping warm. A fast two hour drive in winter sorted out the men from the boys, no kidding.

Every town had a number one meeting place. Somewhere you would all meet up on a Saturday morning and plan out the weekend's football aggro or the monthly shopping expedition to Manchester. Or you'd have a go at impressing the opposite sex with your new gear bought on the last trip. We had Selfridges, in the basement of Lewis' department store. A vast open cafe where just about everyone went to strut around and let the world know that they had arrived on the scene in a big way.

We all spent many hours in there, engaging in the teenage mating ritual or marking out your ground with some local hardcase who was about to get his head kicked in. It was the coolest start to the weekend. Jump in the bath to freshen up after last night's beer intake. Get your gear on, splash on the aftershave, and you'd be off down to Selfridges.

And she would be there. The one girl you had been watching for the last few weeks, but were too scared to ask out. The only girl for you. The one that had been driving you mad in bed, your right hand numb as you exhausted every sexual possibility your imagination conjured up. You would follow her around for weeks like a mad deranged dog on heat, hoping she would notice you. Stand next to her at the counter thinking of a knock out opening line that would win her over. Like a mug, you'd even told your mates that you fancied her like mad, but your bottle went every time you told yourself to go for it.

Next time, you tell yourself. *Next fuckin' time I'm going to pull her for sure.*

You then spent weeks attempting to familiarise yourself with her movements. You found out if she was seeing anybody else and all that.

26

She had been at Selfridges for the last ten Saturday mornings, so the next time you'd definitely ask her out. No ifs or buts.

This is the one. You are going to go straight up to her and tell her you fancy her like mad, praying she will come out with you for a night. Only hope that she is on her own and not with all those silly giggling mates she knocks around with. You walk into town looking the business. Your Martens are polished to perfection. Turned up and ironed Levi's. Your best Ben Sherman and black crombie. This time she is going to be yours for sure. How can she resist you? She's there for the taking as soon as she gets an eyeful of Joe Cool.

You walk into a packed Selfridges with your mates, pulse racing and legs shaking. It's a quick up periscope to see if you can spot her and it's bingo! There she is. The girl of your dreams and a fair few of your fantasies. Only trouble is, she is with her mates. The ones that think you are a total jerk-off.

Fuck it. What do they know anyway?

You get your cup of Cappuccino froth and sit down at a table near her's. Sipping your coffee as your mates rib you about losing your bottle again. "Fuck you lot. I haven't lost it. I'll sort it, you see if I don't."

"Bollocks you will!" they shout back, laughing their heads off at the predicament you are in.

With angry promises of "I'll show you fuckin' lot a thing or two about pulling birds", you get to your feet and with your heart in your mouth you walk over to where she is sitting.

Your presence stops the giggling quartet's conversation dead, and you deliver your opening line to the girl who has had you in bits the last few weeks. "I've seen you around quite a bit. Here and there, and I wondered if you fancied coming out with me for a night out. Few beers and a club. What do you say?"

Her friends look at her and begin to giggle, as she looks you up and down with those come to bed eyes and delivers her answer. "No chance. You just aren't my type. Sorry."

And then she joins in with the giggles as you return to your table and your cup of Cappuccino, red faced and as angry as fuck. You wish you could be beamed up as your mates howl with laughter and ask, "How did you go on then? Is she up for it or what?"

A question they already know the answer to by the look on your face.

"Fuck off you lot. Just fuck off and die will yer!"

Blackpool's pub and club scene has always catered for all tastes from the filofax and mobile phone brigade through to football thugs. Think of it and there has probably been a club for it in Blackpool. The club scene in the Blackpool of the Seventies was much better than what's on offer these days though. Much more diverse, but that could be because the music was far richer in diversity then. Not all track suits, trainers, and electronic music to do your head in. You could experience the whole scene from straight to gay on any night of the week.

If you wanted gay, then Lucies bar was the place to head for, with the flamboyant overweight Ivor at the organ to entertain you. It was all brothel look in those days. Dark red and white striped flock wallpaper and buttoned red draylon everywhere. Like something out of *Cabaret*, but it was a good atmosphere down there, providing you had the right mental attitude. Occasionally, the grockles would venture down into the basement with their crew cuts and grinning faces, sniggering behind their pints of lager. Have a look at the queers and maybe kick fuck out of a few of them before heading back to the boarding house, heroes for the night. And they'd get back to Yorkshire or Geordieland and tell their mates how they beat the shit out of the Blackpool queers one night.

But it didn't always go the way they had planned it. Sometimes they were the ones on the end of a good kicking, and some of them learned that not all of Lucies' clientele were of the effeminate, lipsticked, sequinned dress variety. Some of them were big guys who could hit with the best of them, and many of these narrow minded homophobes made their exit from Lucies minus front teeth, and considerably more red faced than when they had entered the bar. Some of the Blackpool queers were no pushover after all.

You did get the queens down there - after all where else had they have to go? Lucies was their second home and a club that offered a friendly hand to anyone, providing they had the right attitude. They always played up to the straights in an attempt to shock us with their antics. Sometimes it failed to work, but other times, it hit the right spot. I was seeing a girl at the time who wanted to go down to Lucies and see what it was all about. So we're down there one night stood at the bar in a packed crowd. She had that puzzled look of embarrassment on her face that told me she had seen enough of Lucies as she sipped nervously from her half of lager.

I nudged her and pointed with my eyes to one of the weirdest scenes I've ever witnessed in public. At a table sat a male Barbara Streisand lookalike, decked out in the full drag. Wig, dress, make up, high heels, the lot. Next to him sat a guy in a black tee shirt, head rolling about all over the place and eyes closed as if he was having the trip of a lifetime. The Streisand replicant was grinning all over her face obviously well pleased that they had our attention.

As I checked out the guy with the rotating head, I noticed a pair of feet and an arse sticking out from below the table. I thought, *No he couldn't be.* But in a few seconds, the guy next to Streisand shuddered and jerked in a spasm-like motion as if he had just shot his load under the table. *No way,* I thought. *That couldn't happen even in Tinseltown.* But it turned out that the arse and legs under the table had in fact given the rotating head a blow job. Streisand nudged his friend who had returned to reality, and pointed out that he had an audience. My girlfriend was bright red shocked by this time, and suggested we do a quick exit. As we were leaving Ms. Streisand shouted to us, "Enjoy the floorshow did you?"

I smiled back as he added, "Do come again, darlings", and laughed at us all the way up the stairs. That was one crazy night, but sadly it did nothing to inspire my girlfriend to re-enact a similar situation back home.

Across the road from Lucies was the famous Yates Wine Lodge, known more commonly as The Yacht Club. It was rough and ready in there, with bare wooden floors, old bars and huge wooden barrels full of all the stuff needed to get you out of your tree. And the famous roast beef and pickle sandwiches served up on a silver platter by a guy who looked like an extra from *The Munsters.*

It was one of the few places where the down and outs could go for a beer or a short. Self styled leader of the Doss Army was a man known as Dixie. A plump man, grey haired, and always wearing an off white raincoat and holding a bottle in his hand. We all adopted Dixie, and the police also looked after him with an unusual degree of care. When he died, it turned out that the much loved gentleman of the road was a war hero, decorated after the battle of El Alamein, and so he was buried with military honours. A nice gesture from the town to one of its more wayward citizens.

Then some high flyer with computer aided design decided to give Yates' the upmarket look. It killed all of the essential character of the place, and all the old dossers were banned from drinking there.

Another fine example of Blackpool progress and its attempts to get away from what made it the top seaside resort.

Also in Talbot Square was the Scotch Bar. It's gone now, but in the Seventies it established itself as the drinking headquarters of the Scots during their summer invasion of the town. They used to invade the town every year for two weeks - the Scotch fortnight - and even brought their own cops with them. That way, the trouble heads could be sorted out by cops who knew their faces, and who would put them back on the train home the following morning. Come closing time at the Scotch Bar, the Tartan Army would disperse and go for a stroll along the promenade to meet up with fellow drunken countrymen to see how much damage and terror they could cause in one night.

And that was another scene. The Blackpool promenade in the early Seventies. It's fairly civilised these days, but back then it was a seven mile long battleground, where hordes of boozed up youths clashed with one another. Cops were always out in force late at night looking to stop the inevitable aggro. It was dangerous on the prom because drunken mobs strolled up and down still holding their beer glasses. The chunky ones with the dimples in. Thick and heavy and very handy in a scrap.

Mass mobs of youths would gather. The atmosphere would go through the roof as they confronted each other to see if one mob would back down. If both stayed for the aggro, then it would kick off and what ensued would be a vicious pitched battle that would end with the plods' Alsatians being let loose to bite the arses off the offenders before arrests were made.

"Oh I do like to be beside the seaside. Oh I do like to be beside the sea. Oh I do like to stroll along the prom, prom prom, where the brass bands play, tiddly - om - pom - pom."

Well you wouldn't have found any brass bands playing on that promenade in the Seventies come chucking out time.

There was the Jager Bierkeller too. A basement drinking den done up in a mock German theme, complete with long wooden benches and tables, and suitably attired frauleins serving up litre glasses of foaming beer. A lederhosened compere led the crowd through German beer drinking songs like *Ein Prosit*, but the glasses were anything but plastic and it was just as violent down in the Bierkeller.

The nightclub scene was a much more safer option to take if you wanted to take the night into the early hours of the morning. There was the Adam and Eve, known to locals as the Adam. It was a designer club for designer people with stainless steel and smoked glass

30

everywhere. Some evenings, it was harder to get into than the SAS. All the local celebs and weekend millionaires used the Adam, and it held the top spot on the club scene for years.

The Revolution, above Jenks bar, was a much more down to earth club with a wider, more alternative clientele. It attracted the heavy rock crowd, the skinheads, the Bowie and Roxy lot, and the glam rockers. The Roxy crowd were well cool and looked the business, especially the girls. Real tongue out stuff as they took to the dancefloor in their immaculately seductive fashion. All of them looking like they had stepped off the cover of a Roxy Music album. Pillbox hats with veils, tight dresses that showed enough cleavage to keep you hard for months. They all knew it too, and really went for it on the dancefloor as we all looked on spellbound. Some of them went for the military look that Bryan Ferry popularised. Army shirts, black ties and sunglasses, but whatever they wore, the Roxy girls always brightened up a dull evening.

But the saviour of the Blackpool club scene was the world famous boxer, Mr Brian London, with his two clubs the 007 and 008. The 007 became the number one alternative club and he always gave preference to the locals, a policy most clubs refused to do. They didn't want to know about Blackpool's natives during the summer, but begged them to come in during the winter when business was shit. Within a short space of time, the 007 became the place to be, and continued to be so well into the Eighties until a mysterious fire closed it down.

There was a hell of a night down in the club when the Royal Marines paid a visit. Apparently one of their mates had been dragged into the street by the bouncers a couple of months before and been kicked half unconscious before the cops arrived, and it was now payback time. A couple of well groomed guys appeared in the club and asked a few of us questions about the incident.

They bided their time until the dinner suited doormen went into the toilets, and then the Marines followed them in, while another held the door in case there was a repeat of the past incident. Some of the locals felt it their duty to have a go, but they thought twice about it that night as the Marines set about getting revenge.

Eventually, Brian London appeared and managed to sort out the nasty situation. The lights went on and the music died while negotiations took place and the Marines left the club happy, with a job well done look on their faces. The two bouncers were left with smashed up, blood soaked faces, similar to how they had left that Marine a few months previous.

Right up until the club's closure, the 007 remained the place to be and was a cultural magnet for all the arty eccentric characters who lived in the town. And they didn't come more arty and eccentric than Cads. A weird guy and a bit of a local hardcase with it. His obsession was David Bowie, and he went to extraordinary lengths to ape his idol, even though he looked fuck all like him.

Bowie was alien-like, a graceful creature with a curious mix of the male and female in him, but Cads didn't possess any of this. He thought he did and nobody dared tell him different for fear of getting their heads kicked in, but he didn't. He was well over six foot tall, thick set and clumsy with it, but you couldn't convince him that he wasn't David Bowie. For Cads it was too late. Bowie was in him and nothing would deter him from his lifelong quest to perfect his act.

He'd appear in the 007 with full make up and wearing a white sailor suit. Get on the dancefloor and give us all *Port Of Amsterdam* like we'd never seen it before. It was hilarious because he took it to the extreme, and was deadly serious about it all. He was well entertaining though and well worth the odd pint of lager he'd ask you to buy for him after he'd come off the dancefloor soaked in sweat. Well worth it.

He could well have been Blackpool's answer to David Bowie were it not for the fact that a guy called Phil Booth lived in the same town and was the holder of the crown Cads so desperately wanted. You could look at Phil and you would swear that you were looking at the man Bowie himself. It was that close. Cads was only too aware of Phil's presence on the scene, and it would wind him no end whenever Phil turned up to show Cads how it was done in every department. Phil had it in layers what Cads wanted.

Phil did the lot. Joined the fan club. Dressed in exact made to measure copies of clothes that Bowie wore. Dyed and styled his hair the same way Bowie did - that weird orange-pink colour that contrasted sharply with the white ghostly taut reptilian skin stretched over a bony body. Phil also boasted that perfectly defined face with sunken cheekbones, and eyes that looked like they much preferred anything to daylight.

Phil was ultra cool and elegant with it, no matter what the weather was. We met up for a beer one hot sunny afternoon in his favourite hang out, The Crown Bar, in the middle of town. It was roasting, but there was Phil in a suit and ankle length green leather coat, grey fedora and mirrored shades, pulling on a Galoise. Not a single bead of perspiration could be seen on him. It was like sweating was for mere mortals and definitely not for Phil.

It was that day he told me he was bisexual. Just came out with it without hesitation. See if it would do my head in or turn me against him or something. He liked to shock at times. Even with his close mates, he couldn't resist the challenge of doing their heads in. The only thing that was shocking to me was his total openness in the way he delivered his confession to me. But doing things differently was Phil's forte and we still remained the best of friends. I asked him why and he replied that he was bisexual because he wanted to experience everything the great man did.

As is often the case with so many individuals, they can be tortured souls, and Phil Booth was a tortured soul. There was a sad desperate side to Phil that led him to get into drugs in a big way. He did the lot, but he loved heroin and ended his days in a seedy world of dirty, damp, dingy bedsits, littered with fish and chip shop papers and empty syringes. He was hopelessly addicted and it showed. At times he would have this wild shiny glaze in his eyes, and his speech would be slurred and incoherent, but through it all he somehow managed to hang onto his style with a certain degree of dignity.

His ending was well sad. Phil passed away while under Her Majesty's pleasure. He'd stabbed a lowlife drug dealer with an ice pick for taking the piss on a deal one afternoon. I was with him half an hour before he stabbed the guy and he was in an absolute fucking mess. The doctor had told him that he would die in the near future if he didn't sort out his habit. His veins were done in due to all the injections, but Phil knew all that and telling him didn't do the slightest bit of good. Some of the places he'd inject himself to get the required buzz just sickened me, but he was on the edge.

He shook my hand and told me to take care. Then he was gone and the next thing I heard was that he was on the run after killing a drug dealer in some row that got blown up out of all proportion. He was found guilty of manslaughter, and after serving the greater part of his jail sentence, mysteriously died of pneumonia in Wakefield Jail. We all felt shit because we kept promising to go over and see Phil so many times, but were all too hooked up into our own problems. We never did get to see that thin smiling face ever again.

Phil Booth was just one of the crazy twisted sad characters that were born out of the Blackpool drug scene. The town has always had a

33

flourishing scene but in the 1970s, it was a lot easier to get your hands on what you wanted. But without a doubt, one of the craziest people you could meet was the vegetarian, sun-worshipping, festival going, tennis playing, guitarist and acid freak, Chris Muir who was Blackpool's answer to Catweazle.

Chris wasn't just off the wall. He built the fucking wall. Viv Stanshall with a bit of Kwai Chang Caine thrown in for good measure. Chris was all this and more. He did drugs with a vengeance after a road accident drastically altered his life. Hit by a driver who failed to stop, he was left lying in a ditch for the better part of three days before being found. Instead of letting time heal his wounds, he let drugs heal them and slowly entered another world where he was the only inhabitant. I mean, people talked of doing eight or ten trips a year but Chris, he did that in a month when he was on form.

You'd see him around town on his old battered bike in his shorts and sandals, and his old canvas gas mask bag round his shoulders with all his essential bits and pieces in. And a home made wooden flute that he'd play to you in-between garbled sentences of complete fucking nonsense that nobody understood. Talked a lot about the music of Steve Hillage and the planet Gong, and flying teapots and head trips, and how the plod were out to get him in a big way. And how he longed to escape from Blackpool, but he couldn't escape because they had built a heavily guarded wall around the whole town and there was no chance of him getting through the checkpoint. Then with a blank look in his eye, he'd be off on his bike with a "See ya".

We all did a lot of tennis in those days. Chilling out under the hot sun with a joint, some cold beers and a few sets of tennis to kill off a perfect day. But to Chris, tennis was a total passion. A way of life as much as his acid was, and he was always ready for a game. Playing tennis with the man was an experience verging on the insanely theatrical, and you'd come off court with your nerves shredded and stressed to bursting. With the game underway, you'd get a ball by ball commentary that lasted the whole match. In between he'd stop to skin one up and then he'd play a set well stoned, which only seemed to increase his skills. He was a cool player and it took a lot to beat him when he was on top form.

And there would be an imaginary crowd and every so often, he would turn to his fans and acknowledge their rapturous applause after he'd produced a particularly brilliant shot. The crowd were on the edge of their seats and you were on the edge of your emotions.

34

And there would be manic fits of anger and deep rage on missing an easy return. He'd go right into one. Total ape-shit and kick the ball over the sun or smash his racket on the court. Just keep pounding away until all that remained were splinters. And he always played barefoot in his tatty old shorts and headband, and the sight of an angry wildly stressed, semi-naked and deeply suntanned Chris Muir in full flight, bearing down on you as you tried to pass him, was something else. Unforgettably nerve wracking.

Certain times of the year, his situation got the better of him and he'd be off to Glastonbury and other festivals. Then he'd be back in Blackpool and he'd go into sudden fits of insanity. You'd be walking down the street with him and suddenly, he'd be in the middle of the road either lying down and ranting and raving or attacking some passing cars, until the plod arrived to move him on or feel his collar.

Other times he'd wander into a busy pub with his dick hanging out, totally straightfaced. He'd walk up to the bar, order a pint and wait until the manager grabbed him and threw him out. Sometimes he'd go peacefully and other times, the manager would have a real handful to deal with. There would be a stream of abuse and a torrent of fists and boots coming from Chris until he tasted concrete. Then out of the blue, when we all thought Chris was going for the straight jacket and ECT, he found a girl who was brave enough to take him on. Settled down and straightened himself out more than he'd done in years. Started up a window cleaning round and last we heard, was doing nicely, thank you very much.

Most of us flirted with drugs such as dope and the occasional barb, but nothing heavier. At the Casino we all used speed like it was going out of fashion but in Blackpool, we stuck to our dope. The so called softer drugs. Regular weekend blowing sessions on a council estate called Grange Park, but known locally as the corned beef island. Soon we were doing it every weekend, and it became the highlight of the week. Everybody came prepared with ample snacks, alcohol and marijuana for the long night ahead.

Cream crackers, an assortment of quality cheeses and bottles of Cinzano Bianco. Drunk ice cold, it was perfect with dope to get us out of our faces. We would eat and drink our fill, get completely stoned via the bong, and almost choke to death as we listened to Monty Python albums until the early hours of the morning. After a good smoke, the laughing would start innocently and build up until everybody was howling in fits of convulsions. It would stop for a few minutes while we gathered air, and then somebody would titter and we'd be off again, and so on and so on until we all passed out.

We used to have this place where we'd go to do a few joints. In the roof space of a large car showroom in Blackpool called Thomas Motors, the local Ford outlet. We'd go out on the usual one. A few beers in town and see a few friends, and then head down to the roof space. It was high up and a hard climb to get in, especially with half a dozen pints of Brew Ten swilling around inside you, but we'd manage it okay. There must have been a good fifty foot between us and the floor below. Pitch black until your eyes became adjusted to the darkness. We'd chill out up there with a couple of cans of lager. Skin up a few joints and reflect on the little we knew about life.

Then we'd play some games. One after another, we would walk along this steel beam supporting the roof. It couldn't have been more than six inches wide and was a total length of forty feet to the other side from where we were. Half pissed and stoned to the bone, each of us would walk the plank so to speak, in the darkness. Feeling our way gingerly, inch by inch, until we reached the other side. Skin up another joint or two, swallow the last of the beer and head back in a worse state than when we'd made the first crossing. Fifty feet up on a six inch beam, in total darkness, and pissed and stoned, is no time to get a panic attack. One mistake and that would be that. Straight to the bottom and splattered across the latest Ford Escort RS 2000 with full rally spec. What a way to end a night, or indeed a life.

Other times we'd just crash out up in the roof space until it was light enough for us to climb down the drainpipe in safety. An early morning joint to get our heads around the fact that we were about to face reality again, and we'd be off down the drainpipe, and home to bed for some well earned kip.

If you wanted live music in those days, then the place to head for was Jenk's. Always busy every night of the week with a top mix of bands playing. Aggro would regularly kick off there, with locals having a go with the grockles, so the management adopted a policy of plastic glasses in an attempt to quell the amount of horrific facial injuries caused by beer fights. Top music in there though, with several bands going on to monster fame, including The Buzzcocks and Magazine to name but two.

The mob responsible for a lot of the trouble at Jenk's, as well as many other incidents in town, was The Rammy Mob, so called because their local was The Ramsden Arms in Blackpool. They all followed

Blackpool FC with undying devotion and as the word spread of their many legendary exploits, their ranks swelled. A 100% mental mob that ran on alcohol, drugs and their "Seasiders!" battle cry. They have quietened down these days as they all approach middle age, but in their day, it was a case of get out of their way or die. Their crimes against humanity were wide ranging from beating up priests to sexually assaulting people of either sex under the piers for a bet. One poor fucker ended up tied up in a wardrobe with the wardrobe face down on the floor after being given some acid to send him on a trip he would never forget. And then there was the hitchhiker who had the bad luck to get a lift from a van full of them going to a football match. He was a hippy, but by the time they had dropped him off, he'd had his head shaved and nearly been fucked up the arse and killed by the insane, psychotic passengers in the van. By all accounts, the poor guy was lucky just to lose his hair as the vibe in the van changed from good hearted humour to murder.

One bank holiday weekend saw them pull up outside the Low Wood, a popular pub in the Lake District that's busy at the best of times, never mind on a bank holiday. There was a disco that afternoon, so The Rammy decided to join in, but their joining in was different to other peoples interpretation of the word and soon they were stripped bollock naked and dancing around the pub with pints firmly clutched in their hands. The football chants soon followed and a few beer glasses got smashed.

A cold atmosphere filled the pub as the locals began to get pissed off by the thugs. The manager decided to call time and also call for the local plod who arrived in a nasty mood. The Rammy stood their ground for a few minutes, but decided to call it a day and leave the pub. They stayed the night on the car park and had a great barbecue so the story goes. They managed to rustle up a few young lambs from the hillsides, slaughtered them, and ate them over the camp fire before heading back to headquarters to tell their tale over foaming pints of beer.

Strangely enough, they weren't around the weekend Manchester United came to town with the Red Army. At the height of their hooligan infamy, United were drawn away to Blackpool in a Cup tie, so it was an ideal opportunity for the Red Army to visit the seaside, and they did just that. They came in their thousands like a pagan marauding army of Vikings to lay siege to the town. A three or four day spree of looting, pillaging and vandalism followed, the like of which, the town has never experienced since.

It was like a well planned military invasion. The advance parties arrived midweek to suss the town out. They were all over the place, and the plods' sirens never stopped wailing as incident followed incident. Looted shops, smashed windows, overturned vehicles. But the plod were hopelessly outnumbered, and proved almost useless in their attempts to stop the Red Army from doing exactly what it wanted to do.

Then the main force arrived at the weekend and took their exploits further. Shopkeepers and boarding house owners were mortified as they could only watch the Red Army terrorise the town. Pub owners refused to serve the United hooligans, but that didn't stop them. They just stormed the bars and served their own beers until the plod turned up. Then there would be trouble before the invaders made their way to the next pub.

At the Pleasure Beach, the jewel in Blackpool's crown, they went on the rampage in a frenzy of wanton destruction in the name of Man Utd FC. Families were sent scattering in terror as the bovver booted army ran amok. They even smashed up the symbol of the Pleasure Beach, The Laughing Man. He just kept laughing so they kicked fuck out of him until he laughed no more.

With him silenced, it was time for the match, so the United fans made their way down to Bloomfield Road. The ground was completely invaded by the Red Army and we all watched United win the match, courtesy of Messrs Best and Law. In a final gesture of contempt they invaded the pitch en masse, dismantled the goalposts and left the ground with them. A souvenir of their weekend at the seaside, and as the last of them pulled out on the football special taking them back to Manchester, the whole town breathed one huge sigh of relief. Not that it bothered me because I was a Red Army man myself. So funnily enough was Ged, the friend who shares so many of the stories in this book. He actually sat on his Mum's knee at Wembley the day Manchester United won the European Cup back in 1968.

For the greater part of the Seventies, the football hooligan reigned supreme. These days the police have almost won the war against football violence, at least inside grounds, thanks to close circuit television cameras and all seater stadiums that make it so much more difficult for aggro to kick off. But in the Seventies, the police were up against it in a big way, and nobody came any bigger than the Red Army.

Large open terraces became fully fledged battlegrounds between opposing mobs of football fans. The grounds featured little or nothing in the way of security. No cameras and no steel fences to keep fans segregated. All you had were large spaces from goalmouth to goalmouth that allowed the hooligan armies complete freedom of movement to do battle.

In towns all over the country, opposing fans would clash in fights lasting from train stations to football grounds, and vice versa after the match had ended. Every Saturday the same scenario would be enacted around the country. Away fans would arrive by train. The home fans would be lying in wait and it would kick off big style. Shop windows would be broken. People injured, or robbed, or both. Plod would get their blue helmeted heads kicked in, and British Rail trains would be totally wrecked. And I mean wrecked. Seats ripped out and thrown through windows. Toilets smashed and the whole train covered in spray paint graffiti. SKINS RULE was painted everywhere you looked, and for a long time it genuinely appeared that the authorities had conceded defeat to the bovver booted army of thugs.

Town centres were put under siege and there was a total disregard for the public's safety, as mobs chased and kicked fuck out of each other until the plod arrived to arrest them. The police did have some success on occasion, but they were not an effective deterrent in the true sense of the word. In fact, the police often became objects of ridicule who were put to flight under a hail of fists and Doc Martens. Fines, if you were unlucky enough to get arrested, were small, and no deterrent whatsoever.

It was a social problem that just grew and grew until the authorities finally began to apply themselves to the problem properly. Old Trafford became the first ground in the country to have metal security fences erected so that the Red Army would be kept at bay. The violence had reached an unacceptably ugly level one afternoon when Leicester City paid a visit to Old Trafford. Somebody from the crowd threw a dart at the goalkeeper and the dart hit him. It stuck in his head and the only reaction from the Red Army were howls of laughter as the keeper was carried off the pitch with the dart still stuck in his skull.

Shortly afterwards the fences went up and the press carried headlines like ANIMALS CAGED AT LAST. Old Trafford became a relatively safe ground, but outside the ground and at away matches, it was a different story. The football hooligan in general became a feared monster, with Man Utd's Red Army the most feared of all. They seemed unstoppable and their appetite for destruction increased both at home and abroad.

"Stretford Enders we are here . . . Oh Oh, Oh Oh,
Stretford Enders we are here . . . Oh Oh, Oh Oh
Stretford Enders we are here,
Shag your women and drink your beer!
Oh Oh, Oh Oh Oh, Oh Oh"

The buzz at Old Trafford was unbeatable. How could it not be with the likes of Denis Law, George Best and Willie Morgan entertaining us with their skills. Old Trafford was the temple of football and was always filled to capacity from the Stretford to the Scoreboard End. In those days crowds of 50-60,000 filled the ground, and the chanting was deafening at times as everyone got behind the Reds.

You always thought they couldn't be beat. No matter how shit they played (and on occasion, even United played shit), you just believed in them. People like Bestie, a pure soccer pop-star, could win a game in a second of sheer brilliance if he wanted to. Turn the game round from defeat to victory at the last minute as the ref put the whistle up to his mouth.

Whenever the opposing team scored a goal against United at Old Trafford it would be greeted with a deathly silence, as if someone had died. The away fans would be in raptures at their team's success and that would be that. Within seconds the aggro kicked off and United fans were into them.

"Hello . . . Hello . . . United aggro . . . United aggro . . . Hello . . . Hello."

If it looked like the unthinkable was about to happen, the fans in the Stretford End would make their way around the ground to the aggro in the Scoreboard End. Thousands of them singing the death march and spilling onto the pitch or climbing over seated spectators to wage war with the opposing fans.

Then they put the fences up and Old Trafford became a haven of safety and all the fun stopped. Two things United fans hated and that was Chelsea and more than them, Liverpool. We'd go to Anfield, that shithole of a ground, and be confronted with a mob of hungry looking Scousers holding up banners proclaiming MUNICH 58, the year

United's Busby Babes were killed in an air disaster. Then they would come to Old Trafford and it would be "Shankly no more", and so on and so on. Sick humour that really only reflected a tiny percentage of the deep rooted hatred each had for the other.

Nobody was into going to Anfield, especially for a night match but then again, the Scousers hated coming to Old Trafford. But one night, we did pay a visit to Anfield. It was packed out and the buzz was electric to say the least. All the tension and the usual pre-match slanging had started. "We hate United . . . we hate United"' and "Fuck off Scousers . . . fuck off Scousers". It was pissing down, windy, and a pain in the arse to be there.

Suddenly this young United fan jumped out from the crowd, through the cops and onto the pitch, and began charging towards the Kop. He reached the goalmouth and took out a Liverpool scarf and, in a mocking gesture, proceeded to wipe his arse with it. He threw it to the ground and stamped all over the thing, before throwing the Kop a defiant fuck you sign and making his way back to the away end.

The blue helmets were all converging on him to make the big arrest, but the youth was having none of it. He was like lightning and managed to dodge and weave his way through several stupid looking plod. One went down on his arse as all the United end got behind the lone fan, willing him on to make it to the safety of the United lines. It was almost as good as watching George Best at his best as he weaved his way through.

"Come on you Red . . . Come on you Red . . . Come on you Red!" was the chant going around the ground as he got nearer. One more plod to go and he'd be home safe. The plod was determined to bring him down. He dived at his body in a rugby style tackle, but was nowhere near. He got to the terrace, jumped the wall and vanished into the crowd, swamped by United fans who were protecting him from the plod.

The plod who had attempted to tackle him ended up with his smart blue uniform covered in Anfield mud. As he got to his feet, the crowd greeted him with, "Who's that feller in the pointy hat? Do-da, Do-da, Who's that feller in the pointy hat? Copper is his name!"

Government recognition of the trouble the Red Army caused when they travelled to other towns was there for all to see when United got to Wembley against Southampton. At the time, they were at the peak of their reign and somehow had to be stopped. After all, the Government couldn't afford to have thousands of football hooligans wandering around the capital, terrorising people. Especially northern football hooligans. That just wouldn't be acceptable.

As expected, thousands turned up outside the ground to see their heroes. Many hundreds of fans didn't have tickets, but still expected to get into the ground to watch the match. In those situations it would be a case of kicking down the gates or scaling the walls to get in, but Wembley was a little different than your average ground. Higher walls, built like a fortress, so that was out. But to make absolutely sure the ticketless Reds couldn't get in, the Government sent in the Parachute Regiment to stand guard over every entrance. Instead of watching Paddy over in Northern Ireland, they were now guarding the next biggest threat - the Red Army. They were everywhere with these monster Alsatians, just itching to be let loose on the fans. Barking madly and with these evil looking teeth, and that was just the Paras. I mean you, wouldn't think of fucking with a war dog, but every now and then, a brick would be thrown at the red berets, the gates would open and a scuffle would kick off between United fans and the tough looking Paras.

The police bore the brunt of most Saturday afternoon aggro. After all, they were at the cutting edge of the system so were expected to keep law and order, no matter how dangerous it got. They didn't really want to be there, wedged in between two armies of opposing fans ready to kick each other's heads in, but duty called. They would be ordered in, hopelessly outnumbered, to quell the violence on the terraces, only to be put to flight under a hail of bottles, bricks and boots.

It wasn't always like that though. Sometimes you would end up in the back of a plod Transit van, waiting for the kicking that would surely come. And frequently, they did manage to stop the aggro. Steam in team handed, grab the leader and get him out of the ground as quickly as possible. But more often than not, the presence of the thin blue line on a packed terrace was greeted with a torrent of abuse from everyone concerned. Nobody gave a fuck that the plod were all around. Threat of arrest and all that. No one gave a toss because the blue uniform wasn't taken seriously at all.

One weekend we travelled to Derby and the Baseball Ground. We travelled down on the train and waited with a bunch of other United fans until the bulk of the Red Army arrived at the station. There were thousands of us in the town and after the usual pre-match scuffles, we made our way to the ground. We took our place in a packed out ground, and were soon confronted by a sizeable mob of Derby fans wanting to have a go. They started chanting at us and we responded with "Fuck off Derby . . . Fuck off Derby", and the standard, "You're gonna get your fuckin' heads kicked in!"

A few preliminary skirmishes took place as we both swayed into one another. Fists and boots and all that carry on. The tension heightened as we all sensed it could be a big one, so the plod moved in to sort it out quickly. They split us up and started weeding out obvious trouble makers. They got some of the Derby fans, but when it came to taking a few United fans, they were beaten back and a few of them lost their helmets to the Red Army.

The situation calmed as the match began, and the plod kept us apart with two or three rows of them standing between the rival fans. Then a United fan produced a spray paint can and craftily managed to write MUFC in big bold red letters on the back of one of the copper's black raincoats. It looked great and the plod didn't have a clue it had happened.

After finishing his handiwork, the United fan disappeared into the safety of the crowd who were by now in hysterics. The dopey plod kept turning round to see what all the fun was about which made the situation even more hilarious. It must have been a good half an hour before an irate peak cap arrived to reprimand the unsuspecting copper and tell him to go and remove the offending garment and replace it with something more in keeping with the image of the British bobby.

Neck and neck with the infatuation for looking cool and running riot on football terraces came music, and there was plenty of choice available to cater for all tastes. The heavy rock crowd had among others, Deep Purple, Black Sabbath, and Led Zeppelin to get them at it. The bikers head-banged away to Status Quo, who weren't always the "every record sounds the same as the last one" band they have been of recent years. And there was Motorhead, at one time the loudest band in the world with the fiercesome looking Lemmy fronting them. The Rolling Stones were well and truly there as they are these days, twenty years on. Among their musical repertoire in those days was *Honky Tonk Women*, *Angie*, *Let's Spend The Night Together* and many other memorable classics from arguably rock's greatest outfit.

Rod "The Mod" Stewart was up there with the best of them and responsible for some credible early albums like *Every Picture Tells A Story* and *An Old Raincoat Never Let's You Down*. Prior to his success under his own name, Rod had been the driving force behind The Faces, along with his old mate Ronnie Woods, who later became a Rolling

Stone. Spikey hair, spikey noses and unmistakably cheeky grins were the trademarks of The Faces' two talented frontmen. They were a good band, steeped in rhythm and blues, and humorous to on occasion as *Lazy Sunday Afternoon* proved.

The hippies and stoneheads had bands like Genesis, Yes, Pink Floyd and Hawkwind to relax and expand their minds to in dark dope filled rooms. Genesis, fronted by the brilliant Pete Gabriel, established themselves as a talented rock band with a sense of the theatrical. Many of their early concerts featuring Gabriel in bizarre guises that left the audiences spellbound. He eventually split the band and left Phil Collins to pick up the pieces, which he did with 100% success. Gabriel was a hard act to follow, but Collins did it with the album *Trick Of The Tail*. An album perfect for dope smoking. Who hasn't listened to that album in their bedroom, in the dark, all alone, and drifting off to never never land after smoking a big fat joint? And that other dope smoking classic of an album, *Dark Side Of The Moon* by Floyd. Just about everybody must have done a few joints listening to that one crashed out on someone's lounge floor.

The Glitter / Glam crowd had the irrepressible Garry Glitter as the leader of their gold and silver lame, stacked heel movement. He burst onto our television screens on a Thursday night with his first big hit - *Rock N Roll*, and went on to further fame and success with *Do You Wanna Touch Me*, *Do You Wanna Be In My Gang*, and *Hey Rock And Roll*. He's still around too and his Christmas extravaganzas are something to be experienced. He still bangs it out with all the enthusiasm he ever had.

Following on in the footsteps of the Big G were Sweet, complete with long blonde hair and make up. They had a series of hits in the Seventies, including unforgettable numbers such as *Blockbuster*, *Coco*, and their anthem, *Ballroom Blitz*. The genius of Marc Bolan and Tyrannosaurus Rex surfaced with the hit *Ride A White Swan* in the early Seventies, with the charismatic Mickey Finn on congas. T. Rex were a good band, combining glam with serious talent, and went on to have further success with the likes of *Jeepster*, *Hot Love*, *Deborah*, *Children Of The Revolution*. And just at their peak, it all suddenly ended with the death of Marc Bolan after his car crashed into a tree. He was a class act and without doubt, one of the finest singer-songwriters to come out of this country.

Also flying high was Bryan Ferry and Roxy Music who burst onto the pop scene with their classic *Virginia Plain*. From initial glam rock beginnings, Ferry, together with Eno, Manzahera, and the crazy saxophonist Andy Mackay, went on to make some fantastic music, but Ferry eventually called it a day with Roxy and went solo. Bryan Ferry metamorphosed from a silver cat suited made up singer into a suave, sophisticated, slick backed crooner who had the pick of any woman he wanted and a penchant for the clothes of Paul Smith. For a time, Ferry was at the pinnacle of rock success. Not bad for a Geordie art student and building site worker.

Then there was the man, who like Bryan Ferry, never seemed to be out of the limelight after the single *Space Oddity* entered the charts. Born David Jones, but better known to his millions of fans as David Bowie. A brilliant multi-talented artist who over the course of his performing life, has changed his persona to fit the particular mood he was in. In the Seventies, Bowie was going through his thin white duke soul period, after finally killing off his androgynous alter ego, Ziggy Stardust, at the Hammersmith Palais in 1972 in front of a spell bound audience.

And for the really sussed, there was soul. Soul music poured out from recording studios all over the States and flooded the UK in both single and album format. The birth of soul can be traced back to the arduous, inhuman days of the slave system and cotton plantations in the Southern states, where black people were treated no better than farm animals. Their sadness and struggles came out in their music and the blues was born. Then jazz came along and established itself as a major art form the world over, and a music that whites readily embraced with passion. As an offshoot of jazz, way-out hipsters like Charlie Parker and Dizzy Gillespie came to dig up a new music. Beebop had arrived on the scene and suddenly everything was cool.

The guys that played beebop were cool. Ultra cool and lethal on their horns. And the crowd that followed and listened to beebop were cool and dressed cool. The zoot suit arrived. Big and baggy and unstructured. Worn with garish silk ties and creased shirts. The image seemed to sum up the drug-using nocturnal lifestyle of audiences and players alike. Fast and underground, and a toke on a joint in between a mouthful of hamburger or a ten minute withering sax solo. What a way to go.

These were the roots from which soul was born. Stax, Atlantic and Tamla Motown all exploded in a big way in the mid Sixties, and soul's massive popularity ensured it was only a matter of time before it made its way over the Atlantic ocean to invade our shores. Soul was everywhere and breathed new life into the UK music scene, although it was the sharp suited scooter riding mods who really claimed it as their own.

As well as Stax, Tamla and Atlantic, there was Philadelphia. A smooth smoochy late night kind of soul from bands like The Three Degrees, The Intruders, The O'Jays and Billy Paul. It was soul music but wimpy soul music, lacking all the guts of the much fuller sound produced by Tamla or Stax, and the quicker uptempo soul that came from Atlantic. Okay if you were a wide brimmed pimp driving down to the sleazy part of town to make sure your girls weren't ripping you off. But otherwise, Philly soul had fuck all to offer you.

And wedged in between the big names was a far less commercial sound that was being played in the clubs. The sound of northern soul. An obscure, infectious type of soul music that was beginning to take off. Similar to Tamla, but less engineered in the studio sense. It had been around since its introduction to the UK in the Sixties and its popularity slowly moved north of the Watford Gap to where it found an eager and receptive audience.

A network of clubs created a unique underground scene that kids couldn't help but get into. Clubs like The Torch in Stoke and The Twisted Wheel in Manchester staged all nighters where kids, topped up on speed, came to dance the night away. All of this was going on and we were more or less oblivious too it. But not for much longer.

I'm On My Way

A mid this plethoric seaside backdrop of looking cool, football aggro, the Okeh scooter crew, eccentricity, and reefer madness, boredom still managed to creep in. Life was telling us that it was time for a change of habit before we got swallowed up in the sea of superficial enjoyment that Blackpool offered us. But what to do and where to go, we hadn't a clue.

That was until we pulled into the car park of a club just outside Blackpool called Gallopers. It was a popular club and attracted a varied clientele, mainly due to the excellent music policy it featured. We parked up the scooters, paid the entrance fee, and stashed our sheepskins and helmets behind the pay desk. We got served at the bar and then searched around for a space in the packed club. They were all in that night. The Bowie crowd, the Roxy crowd, the heavy metal crowd and the usual bunch of normals. The type who can't decide what the fuck they are into. But each mob had their fifteen minutes of fame on the dancefloor as their music was played.

Soon it was the turn of a guy who was well known locally as a DJ. A guy called Pete Haigh who is still on the scene these days and a regular writer for *Blues And Soul* magazine. He has lived and breathed music all his life, and no doubt will continue to do so until his dying day. That night he took the decks and played the very first northern soul track I ever heard, *If You Ask Me* by Gerry Williams, which was followed by *Love On A Mountain Top* by Robert Knight. It was all so different, so refreshing to listen to, that it grabbed me by the throat there and then and refused to let go.

It was soul music, but not the Tamla type, or Atlantic or Stax. It had a raw energy that made it distinctive from all that other soul, good as it was. The tempo, the driving beat, the bass and the brass all seemed to flow out from the speakers and get right into my head. A sound that had its own originality and power, and a magnetism that pulled you towards the dancefloor time and time again. It was soul music made for dancing, and dance we did that night at Gallopers, even though we weren't familiar with the music and how to dance to northern soul. But we soon learned all the right moves.

The desire for something fresh and new was already inside us. We just needed somewhere to go to fill the appetite so unexpectedly created by the music in that club that night. All we had to do was find the venues, and it was fortunate that we didn't have to search very hard for them at all.

The northern scene was alive and kicking in Blackpool, although largely undiscovered to those not in the know. The Highland Room was the centre of it all, but there were also other clubs you could go to and listen to northern. There was Gallopers at Cleveleys, and the Peacock Room, a large room at the back of The Welcome Pub that staged some excellent soul nights at the weekend. And the Casino building in the Pleasure Beach complex put on regular weekly nights that were always kicking.

The Blackpool Casino became the number one meeting spot the night before Wigan, and a focal point of the scene. People would meet up and sort out all the little details before the all nighter. Things that could totally fuck up your all nighter if they didn't get sorted. Arranging a lift and sorting out the drugs. The usual kind of thing. But that's not all that went on in the Casino. You could get an earful of the coolest northern sounds around, thanks to the brilliant Baz Stanton, the man behind the decks. Without Baz spinning the tunes, the atmosphere would have been pretty crap, but his taste in northern always kept the dancefloor full with people trying out their footwork before they got out on the Wigan dancefloor.

All the main faces went to the Blackpool Casino and there were none crazier than Rick Glancey from St Annes. Rick was cool and could dance better than he could walk. Just to watch him go through his routine was a pleasure to witness. He appeared to float around the dancefloor with uncanny ease, looking like an insane Joe 90 on acid. Thick rimmed glasses and a permanent grin on his boat race. Rick had a monster appetite for drugs and some nights he'd take so many, you could hear the guy rattle as he danced past you. He had bottles of assorted gear and we all wondered how the fuck he was managing to consistently come up with quality gear, but when he told us that his old man was a chemist, it all became as clear as daylight. He had some rough times, but he came through them all okay and lives a much quieter and sleepier life these days.

And then there was the Highland Room on Central Drive, right at the top of the Mecca complex. A much respected northern venue, and always packed despite the fact that it hadn't got an all night licence. Everybody used to go up to the small intimate room to soak up the vibes of a busy northern night. Ian Levine, Colin Curtis and Tony Jebb were the men behind the decks and all three did a top job in making the venue the place it was.

Levine came from a wealthy local family and was always jetting off across the Atlantic in search of northern sounds to play to his eager audience. His was a large contribution to the northern scene and he has gone on to bigger and better things these days, producing many big recording artists. But he will always be associated with the Highland Room whenever there is talk of it, and you can't help thinking that one day he might be back on the northern scene now that interest is beginning to simmer once again.

It was something else in there. It was a small, almost cosy room and had a tremendously faithful following. Always full to bursting and never far away from the long arm of the law. It used to get up their noses that so many people were having such a good time with the minimum of aggro. On a hot summer's night, the buzz was electric. The dancefloor was packed and gear would be going around the place like there was no tomorrow. The drug scene was uncontrollable and the plod knew this. Every now and then, they would keep us on our toes with surprise visits in the hope of catching a few people either dropping gear or selling it. They would burst in and the dancefloor would rapidly empty. All that was left on it were hundreds of assorted capsules and crushed tablets.

Gear was cheap so in a situation like that, you would get rid of your supply, and when the pointed hats had gone, buy some more. The plod would give us all a sermon about what was going on in the Highland Room, and that next time there would be plenty of arrests and that was definite. All frightening stuff. And then they would leave and it would kick off again. The lights would go down, the music would start and we'd be at it as if they had never interrupted us.

It was during early '74 that the northern scene really did go through the roof in Blackpool and just about everybody we knew was into it. An old beat up club in Victoria Street opened up under the name of Scoeys and its policy was strictly northern. An admirable gesture, but a short lived one as the management realised that in order to stay open for business, he'd have to drop the strictly northern and widen the clientele.

That was okay though because it was a large club with several dancefloors, one on each floor in fact. We had the top one all to ourselves so it was nearly as cool as having the place to ourselves.

Scoeys turned out to be a sanctuary. A little home from home. A place you could go to on a Saturday afternoon. Have a coffee and listen to the sounds on the jukebox, and if you were sneaky, skin up a joint, get stoned and watch all the hustle and bustle of a Blackpool in season.

It was in Scoeys that rumours began to filter through about an old ballroom in Wigan taking over the scene. Apparently, it played nothing but northern and was open all night too. It had only been open about six months, but was already packing them in like you wouldn't believe. They were coming from just about everywhere in the country to be at the all nighters. A few of our mates on the scene had been to Wigan and said it was like nothing else they'd experienced before. A totally new scene that ran on music, friendship and speed. It all sounded too much, but a fucking brilliant too much. Like a new fresh youth culture was starting up, so we began thinking seriously about going to Wigan.

Then one lazy afternoon in Scoeys we saw an advertisement pinned up on the notice board saying that a coach was running from the club to Wigan Casino, and that there were seats available. Deposits were required to reserve a place, and it also said that the Casino was a members only club so postal applications had to be made to get a card. All very technical stuff but after a brief discussion, we were all up for it. We paid the £5 deposit and got the Casino's address from the man behind the desk to send off for our memberships.

About a week later, the membership card dropped through the door and that was it. I was now a member of Wigan Casino Soul Club and I hadn't even been there yet. It was then into town to buy a black Adidas sports bag, a couple of spare towels, and the essential deodorant aerosol to keep me cool in the heat of it. A few telephone calls confirmed that the others had received their cards and plans were made to meet up for a few beers before catching the coach. Usual sort of stuff, but that night it was anything but usual as it was going to be our first all nighter and the buzz was well different. Even though we hadn't set foot in Wigan Casino yet, we knew we would be into it and that our time in Blackpool was over. We'd all successfully graduated from the university of seasideology and enough was enough.

We finished off the beer, bought a few bottles of cider for the drive down, and boarded the coach for the Casino. It was a boiling hot night, but Wigan wasn't too stressful a place to get to from Blackpool. About a forty five minute shoot down the motorway and you were there. Before we knew it we were leaving the M6 and crawling up Wigan High Street and into Station Road where the coach pulled up outside a large shabby looking red brick building where a mob of people had gathered. A large sign fixed to the building proclaimed Wigan Casino.

We were here at last. The Casino just wasn't like anything you got in Blackpool and looking at it and its age, it probably would have been pulled down and replaced with some fun structure. Can't have anything too old in Blackpool, except the old fuckers who run the place.

The Casino, or the Empress Ballroom as it was officially known, certainly didn't ooze style. Joe Public must have wondered what the fuck was going on in there that made people queue up for hours every Saturday night because it was shabby and dirty looking from the outside, and was barely a shadow of its former self when it was first built in 1916.

The Empress had taken over three and a half years to build, and the original intention was for the building to equal anything the other towns of Lancashire had to offer their public in the way of places of entertainment. The main ballroom was very gracious and airy. A total of one hundred and twenty feet in length, seventy five feet in width and some thirty five feet from floor to ceiling. The interior was decorated in the style of that bygone era. Ornamental plasterwork with paint and gilding applied over it to give it that touch of regal splendour.

The actual dancefloor was constructed of polished maple boards sprung on to a steel frame seventy feet long by fifty four feet wide. According to a newspaper article of the day it had enough room to accommodate a total of three hundred and fifty dancers at any one time. But that was then. When the Empress became the Casino Soul Club there were two or three times that number of heads on those old but cherished and polished boards. And some nights, even more.

The actual hall was built to hold a total of two thousand people and it was very grand. There was a large promenade area each side of the dancefloor where people could stroll around if they were not in the mood for dancing, and over the entrance to the main hall was a large spectators' gallery where you could relax with a pint and check out the activity below.

The official opening ceremony was conducted by the mayor of Wigan, Mr J.T. Anson, with the usual assortment of civil dignitaries in tow, on 1st November, 1916, at six in the evening. The newspaper

51

reported that a meal was provided for those in attendance and the mood was good, despite news of huge losses on the Western Front.

Sometime later, a large annexe was added to accommodate the ever increasing numbers of people that were flocking to the Empress each week. With the addition of this and a new upper balcony, you could now walk right around the hall from the upstairs, and this annexe came to be known as Mister M's to the northern soul faithful. A little Casino within a larger Casino and a place where some of the best northern sounds were ever put down on record decks.

Over the years, use of the Empress Hall declined, but the place saw it all as each successive generation danced to their own music. The dance band era, rock and roll, and the punks all did their bit on the Empress dancefloor. But the real decline had come in the Sixties, with the arrival of the discotheque. As these spread across the country like lightning, the Empress suffered the fate of so many of the once popular dancehalls. Relegation to bingo hall status and the Saturday night disco. But at least it was saved from the demolition contractors.

Eventually it did keep its appointment with the iron ball, but at least the Empress went out on a high note as a place that had meant so much to so many people up and down the country in its guise as Wigan Casino. Better to be knocked down than permanently relegated to a venue staging bingo nights where comperes shouted out numbers to an assortment of fat old women waiting for the big one. Few would have predicted that the Empress would rise again as an entertainment venue and be packed out with people on a weekly basis enjoying themselves. Back in use once again as a dancehall. And even the guy who came up with the idea to stage all nighters there could not have conceived the numbers of people who would become members as a result of his efforts.

It must have been an expectant but uncertain Russ Winstanley that stood behind the record decks at two in the morning on the 23rd of September, 1973, and played the very first northern sound that started off the legendary all nighters. *Put Your Arms Around Me* by The Sherrys. By the end of that first nighter, some six hundred heads had taken the trouble to come and see what was going on there, and from that first six hundred, the Casino just grew and grew to having over one hundred thousand members. Some feat that, considering that it all took place in an old run down building stuck in the middle of a dreary industrial town, miles away from the bright lights and razzle dazzle of a big city.

Wigan Casino certainly wasn't trendy. It offered no luxuries or frills or gimmicks to entice punters through the doors. No high tech laser shows. No stainless steel dancefloors with women in cages suspended above you as you danced the night away. No topless barmaids and not even decent toilets.

But what it lacked in those departments, it more than made up for in a spirit and atmosphere that had to be seen and felt to be believed. The atmosphere was generated from those massive speakers and passed on to the punters out on the floor, and it was just brilliant. On a hot summer's night when you were out on a packed dancefloor, shuffling around to *Too Late* or *Help Yourself*. Right in the middle of that unique youth culture. It just could not be beat, and it kept you coming back for more and more. And the live artist nights just stepped things up a gear and took you even higher. The Casino just grew and grew, and soon after establishing itself as a top venue, it started to produce its own magazine called *Northern Noise* and created its own record label, Casino Classics. The club became well and truly organised thanks to Gerry Marshall, one of the best club managers you could wish to meet, the disc jockeys and the bar and door staff. The Casino simply became the place to be if you were into northern and wanted it late.

The coach driver opened the doors to let some fresh air in on our first night in Wigan, but we didn't rush to get off. We sat for a few minutes finishing off the cider and checking out the mob outside the coach. It seemed some of the crowd were annoyed at our presence, and they peered in with angry eyes as if to say here we go again. More pain in the arse strangers to help fuck up our scene. Two nasty looking boneheads in particular were giving us the thousand yard stare that told us our presence was not wanted. Little did we know that we'd be giving the same sort of looks to newcomers six months after establishing ourselves at Wigan. The northern scene was built on friendliness and all it took was a little time to get bedded in before you became accepted as a genuine soulie, and not one of the many beer-soaked culture vultures that descended on the Casino during its glory days.

We eventually made a move and, after collecting our bags from the driver, headed for a cafe next door to the Casino. It was packed out with heads drinking tea and coffee, and the smell of dope was too much as we entered and made our way to the counter to get served. The pies and pasties in that place had to be sampled to believe just how bad a pie could taste, but nobody gave a fuck. Coming down on a cold January morning after an all nighter, when you are skint, knackered, and hoping for a lift back home, those pies were the business.

The cafe was a hotbed for drugs. You could get anything in there from the shifty looking dealers sat at tea stained tables waiting for the stream of punters they knew would appear. The car parks too were top places to score gear, and on any all nighter, you could see clusters of people standing around parked vehicles, discussing what deals were going down. Collars up and hands in pockets, making their minds up if what they were looking at was the right stuff for them. On a busy Saturday night hundreds and hundreds of pounds changed hands on the car parks, and all under the noses of the local plod who didn't seem to care.

On leaving the cafe, we noticed that a lot of heads were disappearing down an entrance where some northern sounds were blasting out. We thought we would take a look, and made our way down a long, dark, crowded corridor that led to a very large and very basic room. Cold and damp with wall to wall concrete, but behind some record decks stood a disc jockey spinning some class northern sounds we'd never heard before.

A few people were dancing but most were sat around just talking or skinning up a joint to chill out before the all nighter kicked off. This room was called The Beachcomber and was the place to be before the all nighter. You could usually tell if the all nighter was going to be a biggie or not by the number of heads in The Beachcomber. It was rough and ready, and freezing cold in winter, but it had a brilliant buzz when it was kicking. Even on a cold February night with no heating and only the people to keep you warm, it was just the place to be. A place to meet your friends, score gear, talk about the week's events and listen to top class northern care of Messrs Cain and Rigby. Your original garage party before all that became trendy and acceptable.

We had time to grab a couple of cans of Coke and talk to a few mates who'd travelled down on the coach before people were on the move, picking up their bags and shaking each other's hands as a parting gesture until they met again in the main hall upstairs. We followed them out into the street and joined the massive queue. The unpleasant weekly ritual that nobody looked forward to. The crowd was horrendous, and you had no room whatsoever to move around in once you were stood in line. You were in it and that was that. With your all nighter bag on your shoulder and people pressed up tight against you. Up your back, your chest and your arse, wall to wall bodies. It was a fucking nightmare, and the minutes turned into hours as you waited until the doors opened up and the bouncers pulled you in after a quick search for gear. Didn't happen all the time, but occasionally they would give you the once over.

Some evenings the queue was exceptionally bad. Like the live appearances and anniversary nights, and you'd be squashed up in the mass of bodies for a couple of hours. But it had to done to get a place in the Casino. It was shit but it just had to done.

Soon it was our turn through the doors that led to the main hall and our first taste of the Wigan flavour. The doormen gave us the once over, checked to see if we had our membership cards, and let us through. We then joined a more relaxed line of heads that led to a paydesk before you got to the main hall. We handed the smiling lady the cash and headed up the stairs to the main hall. Through the doors and into the large hall, already jam packed with people dancing or standing around talking. The Devonnes' *Pick Up My Toys* was playing. Not a particularly brilliant piece of northern, but one that will stick in my head just for the fact that it was the first sound I heard at Wigan.

The buzz and the smell that hit me was like nothing I'd experienced before. A tremendous body heat mixed with the smell of sweat and a hundred aerosol deodorants in the air. A peculiar atmospheric smell that emanated from just about every corner. Every nook and cranny. A smell I will never ever forget and one that was just pure Wigan Casino.

We stood by the dancefloor spellbound for a few minutes, in an attempt to soak up the vibes of the place and to get our bearings. A large cylindrical ultraviolet strip-light hung above the dancefloor, giving everybody a whiter than white glow, except those who were wearing false teeth. You could spot them as soon as they smiled, but otherwise, everybody appeared ghostly under that light. Like hundreds of northern soul phantoms going through the motions on the dancefloor.

Above the floor stood the stage on which the Wigan jocks entertained the punters with their sounds. Winstanley, Searling, Evison, Ellis and other guest disc jockeys who stood there every Saturday night for the better part of eight years.

Soon we were up on the balcony and checking out the action on the dancefloor below us. There was hardly a space available and everyone seemed to be having the time of times. And the dancing. That was in another league. Pure premier league stuff to the dancing we'd all seen and done back on the Blackpool scene. It all looked superbly effortless on the night, but it took a lot of practice before becoming half decent and having the bottle to get out on the floor. Soulies all over the country would sort out their moves in the privacy of their bedrooms, making sure they were foot perfect before stepping out on that floor at an all nighter.

And that dancefloor was something special. The epicentre of a special underground scene. The altar in the temple of northern soul, and everyone treated it as such. The dancers were brilliant and for the first few all nighters, it was just too much to go out and try out your moves. So we watched from the aisles and the balcony in awe until we got back home. Then we practised the routines in private for hours, getting it all right. The footwork. The moves. All spot on so when the time came, we could venture out on the floor fully confident that we were going to do the business as best we could, and not make complete pricks of ourselves by ending up on our arses in front of a packed audience.

You had to make sure you could keep up with the best of them on the night. Get your gear down your neck. Wait for it to bring you up, and then get out there in that seething mass of amphetamined humanity. The floor would be pulsing. Alive with the weight of people on it, and you would find yourself a space and just glide into it with the music, and that would be that. Initiation over, and you'd wonder what all the fuss and worry had been about. But deep down you knew because you were out on the most together dancefloor in the country and that had to be respected.

It was brilliant to watch a good northern dancer go through his routine. From a casual side to side movement, they'd suddenly erupt and go into a series of acrobatics. High kicks, splits, and backdrops, touching the floor from behind with their hands. Up again, then down on all fours. Flip over, come up and then finish the routine with a wicked spin that seemed to last forever. Stop dead. A handclap and back into the side to side footwork without batting an eyelid. It was sheer performance art, and free for everybody to watch. We hung out many a hot and sweaty all nighter on the balcony with a joint and a cold Coke watching it all going on below us.

And that dancefloor was looked after like no other. On more than one occasion we all jumped in to clean it up before the all nighter kicked off. As punk rock took off in a big way, the Empress became host to a weekly punk rock night. All the Wigan punks would gather there and really go for it with a vengeance. Beer fights that would see the dancefloor covered in blood, snot, spunk and broken glasses. The Wigan punks were a wild bunch, and always had a go at us as we queued up for the all nighter. "Fuckin' soulie wankers" and all that would be shouted at us, and then it would kick off. The odd running battle on the car parks, as the punks got it where it hurt them. And other times they would wait in the bushes across the road from the Casino, and they'd shower us with the bricks and bottles until we chased them off, them howling with laughter as we tried to catch them.

On your average punk night, the dancefloor ended up a fucking disaster, and there was nothing for it but to get it all sorted out as quickly as we could. People everywhere would be hard at it. Arranging the tables and chairs, while others jumped on those strange looking vee-shaped brushes and swept the dancefloor clean of all the punk shit. Making sure every bit of glass was swept up and shovelled away. A last check to see if it was all ready, then the lights would dim and Russ Winstanley would kick off the proceedings once again with the first sound of the night.

The balcony area on that first all nighter was just as busy as the dancefloor, so we crawled our way through the crowd to the bar and asked for a pint. "Sorry love, we don't sell beer here. Just soft drinks", was the shocking reply we received from the woman behind the counter. Couldn't believe that one at all. No beer and only soft drinks to quench our thirsts, but we soon sussed out why the Casino didn't serve or see the need for alcohol.

The speed or gear scene had replaced alcohol as the stuff to get you out of it, and that was something we hadn't experienced before, coming from the land of beer. It just wasn't done in Blackpool, but the Casino policy worked perfectly. So with our cold Cokes in hand, we spent some time on the crowded balcony, checking people out and soaking up the scene. Watching as people changed into fresh tee shirts while others leant back on chairs having a joint before they attacked the dancefloor once again, or visited the record stalls at the back of the balcony where you could get your hands on all your favourite sounds.

At the front and to the left of the balcony area was a door leading to a large room from where we could hear some class northern blasting out. This room was Mister M's and was always a popular and cool place to hang out during an all nighter. All through the time the Casino stayed open, Mister M's maintained a reputation for playing the best northern soul you could hear, and was looked on as a room for purists among the soul crowd. A room you could go to and acquire a soul education. Some nights in M's, it was like a sauna, with an appreciative and dedicated audience going through the motions on the small dancefloor. It was a unique room within a unique scene, and is remembered with much fondness by all who sampled its special atmosphere.

That first all nighter was a completely new and bewildering experience for us all and we spent most of the night just wandering around the Casino, taking in the vibes and talking to people who'd been going since it opened. Walking around the main hall, sticking our heads in Mister M's and fighting our way down the stairs, crowded with crashed out exhausted bodies coming down off gear or catching a few zzz's before going back on the dancefloor.

The jockeys played a multitude of northern sounds on that first all nighter. Some already familiar to our ears, but the vast majority were new to them. Instrumentals like *Sugar Baby* by Connie Clark and *Condition Red* by the Baltimore / Ohio Marching Band. And strong vocal sounds like the Wigan classic *Night Owl* by Bobby Paris and *Free For All* by Phillip Mitchell, two Casino sounds that always brought the crowd onto the dancefloor. The sort of music that once inside your head simply refuses to go away.

After what felt like no time at all, the last record of the night was booming out from the speakers. *I'm On My Way* by Dean Parrish. Every all nighter ended with this one and a very appropriate sound it was too. The light filtered through the dirty stained windows above the corner we had sat in all night and that was that. The end of our first all nighter at Wigan Casino. The lights came on and a chorus of loud applause followed in recognition of the way the jockeys had worked so hard to entertain us with all those sounds. We talked awhile as bodies milled around. Talking, shaking hands and writing down addresses and telephone numbers. Some dancers were towelling off the sweat and then changing into fresh dry clothes for the journey home, and others were skinning up joints to chill out after the night's intake of gear. Eyes like car headlights. Full of energy with nowhere to go. It was a strange scene, but we knew we'd be back for more as we picked up our bags and made our way to the exit, down the stairs and into the waiting coach.

We slumped into our seats exhausted and bewildered at what we'd experienced over the last six hours. A totally original underground scene that was such a welcome change from all the seaside shit we'd done in Blackpool during the last three years. It seemed all too much but a fantastic too much. The sights. The sounds and the smells. No aggro and no alcohol. "Fucking brilliant!", was the general opinion as we talked on the way back to Blackpool early that Sunday morning.

The whole vibe was about going away to a club that only opened its doors at two in the morning when the rest of clubland was just going to bye - byes, and to a club that didn't feel the need to serve alcohol. It was also a club packed with people from all parts of the country that had come to listen to the best northern soul you could hear. It was a brilliant nocturnal world away from the punks and the football hooliganism and Blackpool promenade. And a world we lived in for the better part of seven years before the authorities said enough was enough and pulled the plug on Wigan Casino.

As we became immersed in the all nighters at the Casino, and the northern scene in Blackpool, we quickly established a new social way of life. Living each week after boring week, the culmination of which was the all nighter on Saturday. And it was the same for most of the people we knew at Wigan. All of them living frighteningly similar lifestyles, from Cambridge through to Edinburgh. The week usually consisted of getting over the all nighter and staying in from Sunday until Friday. If you'd done too much speed and were still whizzing away, you were glad of the chance to be on your own to come down in your own time in readiness for the weekend. We all came alive at the weekend and went back into our shells until the next one.

Very rarely did we venture out during the week unless it was for something extra special. Something good at the flicks or to turn out and add some support to a local northern night so it kept going, but apart from that, we couldn't be arsed to step out of the house. We'd all changed, but Blackpool hadn't. It was still full of the same old shit, and there was just no point in getting involved in all that nonsense again at any price. They could stick the Pleasure Beach, the Golden Mile and the Promenade right up their money filled arses as far as we were concerned because we were into another world and another lifestyle.

And it was a totally different one too. The people who went to the all nighters seemed so down to earth and weren't out to impress anyone with their way of life as was the norm in the usual clubs and pubs. They had done the impressive bit by getting to the Casino and that was enough. Nobody we came across would sell you one or give you a load of bullshit. It just wouldn't have worked on the northern scene, and besides, you could get that any night of the week in Blackpool's clubland so it was time off at the weekends. They were special and were treated special.

Hardly anybody talked about jobs and earning money or who drove what kind of car. You couldn't impress anyone that way at the Casino because the weekend was a fleeting escape from all that normality. Time was limited and it was used for friendship and enjoyment and nothing else. A brief escape from the world we all lived in six days a week. And besides, time went by so fucking fast at the all nighters that there was hardly enough time to talk about the things you wanted to talk about, never mind any other old bullshit.

There were people with Jags and brand new Fords on the Casino car park. People who had good jobs, or better still, wealthy parents to help them out whenever they needed a quid or two. They were living life to the full, enjoying themselves and good luck to them. And there was also the guy who hadn't a hope of getting a new pair of jeans, never mind a brand new car. He was the unlucky one. Unemployed. Signing on the dole every week and waiting for the cheque to drop through the door. Getting by as best as he could do under tough circumstances. Life for him wasn't glamorous. Just one big pain in the arse. A headful of ideas and ambitions he could do nothing about except hope and dream that one day, it would all be different for him. His was a world of frustration, broken every other week with the arrival of the giro.

No cars and no posh clothes for him. T-shirts and jeans and whatever else he could make do with to keep him warm when he went to Wigan. After the train fare, the entrance fee and a few quid for some gear, that would be his lot until the next time. And off he'd go in the morning, speeding his bollocks off and full of memories of another brilliant all nighter spent at Wigan. Back to the tiny bedroom in the council flat and the signing on and the boredom and frustration of another week and a half. It was tough on him and tough on others. But they got through it all and there he'd be, two weeks later, with his old sportsbag on his shoulder, queuing up outside Wigan, waiting for the doors to open into his world of enjoyment once again.

There were both sides of the coin at Wigan, but once we were through those double doors, and into the main hall and on that dancefloor, we were all equal. All we wanted to do was drop some gear, listen to some class northern, meet some new people and get out on the dancefloor. It was a unique classless movement of people from all parts of the country, just meeting up and getting on with it. Bonded together by their love of the music, the club and the gear. No fuss, no

60

pose and no shit to spoil the vibes the Casino gave off to everyone who gave it a chance.

No aggro whatsoever kicked off in the Casino. Things like that just didn't happen. I mean you never even thought about it. Pretty amazing that fact alone when you think that the all nighters were packed with people from all parts of the country who, under normal Saturday afternoon circumstances, would be kicking the fuck out of each other in the name of their respective football clubs. That mentality of you're gonna get your fuckin' head kicked in because you are from a different part of the country just didn't get a look in at Wigan. The no alcohol policy probably contributed much to this peace and calm, but I like to think it was more than that. There was a genuinely strong prevailing attitude of friendliness that hit you as soon as you walked through the doors. This attitude peaked at the Casino, but was just as healthy at other northern venues. The Highland Room had it. So too The Torch and Twisted Wheel, Samantha's at Sheffield, The Ritz at Manchester, Cleethorpes, and all the other northern venues that contributed to making the scene such a friendly one.

And the circle of friends just grew and grew both locally and at the Casino. Everyone wanted to get in on the northern scene and once you were in, you were in till the end. People looked after you to make sure your all nighter would go with a bang. If you'd had a shit week, no work, the car had broken down or you hadn't any wedge for some gear, then your friends would bale you out with enough of everything to make sure you not only got to the Casino, but had a brilliant time once there. It always worked like that with the Blackpool crew because one day, one of them might be in the same boat. People who remain friends to this day and the type of people you don't have to see every week down the pub to confirm the friendship. Like the ever friendly Mitch who was spotted at a northern soul night put on by the Casino jockey, Richard Searling. Hadn't seen Mitch in years but there he was shaking hands and chatting away as if it was yesterday. And Mark "Airbeds" Eyre, now a respected builder in Blackpool, and so called because of his dancing style. Whenever he was out on the floor it appeared he was just floating on air inches above the dancefloor. And the brilliant Johnny Walker from Blackpool. One of the most stylish, and friendly heads you could wish to meet. And Daz Hall, well liked by everybody on the scene. There was a side to Daz that was totally fucked up and that was his liking for smack, and he eventually died in mysterious circumstances, a shadow of the healthy smiling guy he once was.

And Bob Blackwood. One of the scene's great characters, always immaculately dressed in a blazer, made to measure smart trousers, and polished shoes. He could dance like the devil and was one of the smoothest soul freaks around. Well respected by all who knew him and a walking encyclopaedia of northern soul knowledge. He was well into his drugs and lost it for a long time, but Bob was a prime example of how to come back from the place most of us would never dare spend time in. He got sorted out and is now a successful businessman in Blackpool. He came out of it all a winner, when he could so easily have gone the way of Phil and Daz

And then there was a wacky guy called Andy Pape who did the all nighters for a few years before mysteriously disappearing from Blackpool, never to be seen again by any of us. A crazy character and a great guy, he saved us from many a freezing cold early morning wait for the train after the all nighter by giving us a lift back in his old brown Rover saloon. It was luxury, having a mate with a class set of wheels, and so comfortable to crash out in. Stick some sounds on and skin up and take a slow but enjoyable drive back to tinseltown.

He worked as a trainee manager with the Co-op and hated the job like you wouldn't believe. Always talked about his big plan to have the Co-op over for a load of cash. It was his job to cash up the tills on a weekend and stick it in the safe until Monday morning. The plan was that he was going to shoot off with a case full of cash. Just clear off right out of it and set up somewhere else in the sun.

His plan needed the services of an accomplice to attack him, cosh him over the nut, and make off with the cash. He would raise the alarm, tell the police what had happened, and as soon as the coast was clear, get his slice of the pie and catch a jet out of here. As it turned out, the Co-op was robbed, but no details were released and we never saw or heard of Andy Pape again. To this day, it would be cool to think that he made it and was lying on some sunsoaked beach surrounded by everything that the money from the robbery could bring him. The first northern soul club in Penang would have been just the right vibe for Andy.

There were other unforgettable heads who were all regulars on the northern scene and who we shared so many good times with. Paul Crane and his sister, Andy "Epic" Stevens, Tim Wilson, Rob Brockus, Howard and Lee Gledhill the leather merchants, Ronnie Miscull and Mad Skin. Just too many to mention, but they were all there from start to finish and lived the life every second from the journey to Wigan to the last record of the night.

We'd all meet up in the Station Bar late on a Saturday night, swill a few beers down and jump on the last train from Blackpool. The Casino special for the journey to Wigan. The atmosphere was brilliant as the all nighter was on us once again. Newcomers were welcomed with a can of beer and a joint to put between their lips, and the guards would ask us to stop smoking or move down to second class. Somebody would stick on a portable cassette and there would be dancing and good times had by all until we hit Wigan.

Some nights we'd arrive too early so it was down to the chip shop for a supper before heading up to the open market to set up a party. Stick some sounds on the portable cassette player and in no time at all, there would be a brilliant atmosphere kicking as people came from all over the place to take part until the Casino opened up. It was good in the summer, but in winter, all we could do was huddle together and keep warm waiting for the off. It wasn't all dancing, drugs and hedonism on the northern scene. Sometimes it was shit. Cold, grim and exhausting, but you kept going back for more because it was the place to be and kicked the shit out of what was offered in mainstream clubland. Everybody took the rough with the smooth because when it wasn't just good, it was fucking brilliant.

Winter was a shit time. Cold nights and freezing cold mornings. Real bad to deal with when you have just spent the last eight hours sweating your balls off on the dancefloor, soaked and speeding to the eyeballs. You'd come down the stairs, into the street and the icy greeting would hit you right between the eyes. So it was kit on and head up to the station, if you hadn't found a lift, and spend a couple of hours in agony waiting for the Blackpool train to take you home. Sometimes you'd be there for two or three hours and the waiting room was always packed out with shivering soulies just as cold as you were. The only relief available to keep your mind off your freezing fingers and toes was the early morning papers. The station porters would wheel up trolleys full of all the main papers and you could just help yourself to them. One or two, or as many as you could fit in your all nighter bag. The only plus side to the early morning horrors of Wigan Station.

One particular morning, we dragged ourselves up the stairs to the waiting room and crashed out exhausted on the floor with the others in there. Thoroughly fucked and cold, we just pulled our sheepskins up around our ears and slipped into the big comedown. Waiting for the gear to wear off us so we could get our heads down and sleep. This guy from Blackpool, called Jenks, a local thug and druggie, was sat next to me and looking like death warmed up, shaking and huddled deep into his sheepskin in an effort to keep warm. All of a sudden and without a word of a warning, he'd gone into one. Shaking and convulsing like it's going out of fashion and then came the vomit. Everywhere, blood and sick mixed with dissolved white powder, and it stunk rotten. It just kept coming and coming. This puke all over the place, and it turned out that he'd done twenty six pills that all nighter. He always did it to the limit and the picture of him lying there covered in his own vomit and too fucked to get up and wash it off has stuck with me ever since. I gingerly helped him onto the train and left him to it as we found a compartment and crashed out.

Other times you'd just head off to the swimming baths around the corner from the Casino and spend a few hours chilling out in there with the smell of chlorine under your nose. A lot of the more energetic soul freaks would get their trunks on, jump in and do a few lengths of the baths in an attempt to get the gear out of their system. But for most of us, it was enough to sit there with a can of Coke and a joint for an hour or so, watching all the activity. It was well relaxing in Wigan baths on a Sunday morning. Every so often, plod would stick his head in to fuck the vibes up. Checking out what was going on, and looking for the opportunity to bust a few people before going back to their other pressing duties.

But the real place to be was the front passenger seat of Andy's Rover. Much more civilised, with the heater on full blast and listening to some northern while somebody skinned up a big one to keep us going until we got home, or till we got to the motorway services for some breakfast and conversation. The services cafes were well popular with all the northern crowd, night and day. Of a night time, they'd be packed with people waiting around for the dealers to show. A last ditch chance to score some decent gear before getting to the Casino. If the staff had realised what was going on, they wouldn't have been so nice to all the strange looking people with the wide eyes and long leather coats, making a banquet out of their coffees.

They were good places to meet and get to know people you'd otherwise miss in a packed out all nighter. Time was tight in the Casino and you couldn't spend it talking to all the faces you'd like to get to know, but you had that luxury in the services. Drink coffee, exchange telephone numbers and talk about life away from the Casino.

One of these people was a guy known as Bootlace. We got to know him well in the services, but in the Casino he was a stranger. Tall, quiet and well spoken with a slight trace of a Brummie accent. He always had a smile and a friendly word for us, and whenever the subject of gear arose, he sorted us out about what to do and what not to do. He was well into his speed and told me about smack and to keep off it at all costs. Last time I saw him, he was in the toilets at Charnock Richard services. Stood in front of the mirror, looking the business in a long camel coloured crombie overcoat and quietly combing his hair. We shook hands and he asked me if I was sorted. I told him I was and he told me to have a good one, picked up his bag and split. Sometime later, unconfirmed reports filtered through that this well liked guy had been killed in a car accident, but hopefully the rumours were wrong.

Occasionally, albeit very rarely, you'd come across characters that broke the mould of the traditional soulie seen on the dancefloor. People so untypical of the scene, and three such people were Pete, Rod and their sister Beenie. One night they appeared out of the blue in the Blackpool corner of the Casino with a smile, a handshake and a cultured "hello". They were older than us, in their mid-twenties, and from a wealthy background. Public school educated, with accents to match their pedigree, but that is where it stopped with them. Both Pete and Rod had long black hair and sported beards, and dressed like your average hippie when not at Wigan. They had the lot. Flares, granddad shirts, Afghan coats and scarves, and from their appearance, they would have been much more at home at a Marc Bolan concert than the dancefloor at Wigan. And Beenie looked like some pre-Raphaelite goddess with long crimped hair, a pale ghostly complexion and her long dresses. But at the all nighters they had the baggy chords, sweatshirts, leather shoes and the sportsbags, and could hold their own with the best of them when it came down to it.

We never did manage to find out what Beenie's real name was or what she did, but her brothers were both radio officers in the Merchant Navy and never failed to mesmerise us with exotic tales of far off travel. They'd put in several all nighters in a row, then disappear for a few weeks. And just when you were beginning to wonder where the fuck they were, they turned up in the corner with a joint skinned up ready to catch up on recent events. Wanting to know all about what had been going on at Wigan in their absence.

They were the friendliest trio you could wish to meet, and one Sunday morning they took us back to their parents pub, high up on the moors somewhere in Lancashire. After a storming breakfast, we all went upstairs to the function room. It was fully equipped with a massive sound system so there was only one thing to do. Roll up the carpet, get the shoes on and mess about on the floor to some northern for a couple of hours before heading home. And another time they took us back to their bungalow and really rolled out the red carpet for us. Full breakfast and a selection of tea and coffee, and then the desert to end all deserts. In comes the delectable Beenie with a silver tray, upon which was an assortment of dope from all corners of the world. Temple balls, Thai grass, Lebanese, Moroccan. You name it and it was on that tray for us to smoke, and we had a riotous time doing just that.

A classic surprise at the Casino one night was when they all appeared after one of their long absences with a sportsbag full of gear. The best gear you could swallow and as it was Ged's birthday, they presented him with a plastic bag full of speed and a few ultra rare, hard to get, Purple Hearts. He was completely speechless as they handed him what must have been well over a hundred quids worth of speed with a smile and a handshake. Sadly, shortly after that memorable all nighter, all three of them did one and disappeared from the Wigan scene completely, never to be seen or heard of again. Maybe they had a hand in the Co-Op robbery with Andy, and jetted off to the sun with him.

We really missed the company of those three, especially the times Beenie used to come off the dancefloor soaked in sweat. She'd come over to the corner where we'd be sat, get out a clean top, whip the old one off without a second thought, and spray on some deodorant after towelling off. And all this going on without a bra in sight. Just tits everywhere, get the clean top on and head off into it once again. She was gorgeous and it was always tongue out stuff whenever she came over to change. The girls were just as much a part of the whole Wigan thing as we were, and went the full way, as we all did, without batting an eyelid. They felt totally confident and at ease with themselves in the Casino and were never subjected to the usual late night male chat up bullshit they'd get in other clubs, and were never hassled when the time came to get their top off and freshen up. There were some goddesses there, but nobody ever fucked them about or took the piss out of them. Identical tastes and experiences bred respect for both sexes and that was just one element, one ingredient, in the Wigan cocktail that made the overall scene so orgasmic. The friendship, the music and the gear. Just one of those classic recipes you never ever lose the taste for.

The music played at the Casino was a continual journey of highs and lows and surprises for all concerned. We'd been into the northern scene in Blackpool before going to Wigan, but after a solid year of all nighters, we realised that we'd only just scratched the surface of this music we all came to love at Wigan. We soon got to know what a floater, a stomper and a stormer was. All categories pertaining to the particular nature and feel of a track of music. Something like Larry Santos and *Girl You Got Me Where You Want Me Now* would contain a beat similar to a stomp and the dancefloor would be packed out and pulsing life. And one hundred mile an hour stormers like *Personally* from Bobby Paris or Phillip Mitchell and his monster *Free For All*, they just kept coming at you from those massive black speakers, doing your head in a little more each time you heard them until you knew them inside out to dance to.

It was all soul music, but it was varied soul music and what appealed to some would not appeal to others. Northern allowed you to have choice within a rare uncommercial music and we all had our own personal favourite sounds. Sounds that reflect the personal feelings or situations you found yourself in at the time or whenever. Sounds that will only make sense to you when you think back and say, "yeah, I was doing that when that was doing the rounds". Seeing the love of your life or being laid off from work, music becomes your own personal time calendar when you look back and reflect on the fun you have had. I wonder what tune will come into your head just as the reaper calls your number?

I can remember being up on the balcony talking away to a girl. Right at the front of the balcony, gassing away and waiting for the speed to sort me when Jimmy James' classic, *Help Yourself* comes on and it's the first time I've heard it. That intro from the horn section just ripped my ears out, it was so fresh. And stuck in the queue for the back bar in the main hall. Just stood there for about half an hour, waiting for a Coke and losing my patience. Wanting to get back to the corner and the dancefloor and get at it. But I'm near the front now so no sense in calling it a day. And one of my fave sounds comes on. *I'm Comin' Home In The Morning* by Lou Pride. A Casino monster and one that drags you to the dancefloor, but my tongue is down to my ankles with thirst so I stick with the queue and Lou Pride fades out. Only hope they will play it again sometime in the night. And Rita Dacosta's very appropriate *Don't Bring Me Down* just as I climb into my pit. Body worn out but my head racing away at a thousand miles an hour for the next ten hours or so.

To ask anybody to go through their favourite sounds and come up with a top twenty would be virtually impossible to do. There were just so many unforgettable sounds to pick from that you'd be at it for months trying to decide. If I did attempt to list some of the sounds that mean a lot to me, the following would be in there for sure . . . James Lewis - *Manifesto*, Gene Latter - *Sign On The Dotted Line*, Rock Candy - *Alone With No Love*, Yvonne Baker - *You Didn't Say A Word*, Willy Kendricks - *Change Your Ways*, Carstairs - *It Really Does Hurt Me Girl*, Ann Sexton - *You Been Gone Too Long*, Mitch Ryder - *You Get Your Kicks*, Dean Courtney - *I'll Always Love You*, Jimmy Mack - *My World Is On Fire*, High Keys - *Livin' A Lie*, Hesitations - *I'm Not Built This Way*, Porgy And The Monarchs - *My Heart Cries*, Valentines - *Breakaway*, Watson And Williams - *Too Late*, Lou Pride - *Comin' Home In The Morning*, Joe Hicks - *Don't It Make You Wanna Feel Funky*, NF Porter - *Keep On Keeping On*, Paul Anka - *Can't Help Lovin You*, Tobi Legend - *Time Will Pass You By*, Jimmy James - *Help Yourself*, Phillip Mitchell - *Free For All*, Johnny Bragg - *Talking About Me*, Jimmy Thomas - *Beautiful Night*, Saundra Edwards - *There's Nothing Else To Say* . . .

It could go on and on and on, but it will end there. The above sounds represent some of the finest tracks of northern to come out of those speakers at the Casino over the years we attended the all nighters. The ones that when I hear them instantly evoke a particular memory or even a particular smell or taste. Northern soul was the first music to touch me in a special way, as it was with so many others on the scene. Some of it was sad. Some of it was humorous. Some of it was made purely for dancing and some of it was philosophical. You only have to listen to *Time Will Pass You By* to get the message from that piece of northern, particularly when you consider it is well over a decade since the Casino closed down. Where did all that time go?

Between 1973 and 1976 the northern soul scene really did seem to explode. It was in the newspapers and on the television, and the exposure highlighted the centre of the scene as Wigan Casino. There was a dubious screenplay on the club by a guy who was obviously trying to cash in on all that was happening, and his research was somewhat lacking, but no doubt he made a tidy wedge out of his misguided efforts. Granada Television covered the scene in a well put together documentary in the *This England* series that covered every aspect of the scene far more accurately. You could also read about Wigan Casino in all the newspapers, especially the Sunday tabloids which concentrated on all the sensationalist aspects of the northern scene, and particularly the gear scene. They all wrote articles that made the club out to be a nocturnal den of iniquity, inhabited by vampire-like teenagers who got their kicks by consuming vast amounts of amphetamines, and spent the night on the dancefloor without a break.

There we all were, members of the Casino. Getting on with it and enjoying ourselves to the limit, and as we made our way home in the early morning, our parents were having breakfast and reading about this drug club that we were going to every Saturday night. Talk about making life difficult, you tabloids. There was much more going on at Wigan than just drugs. Admittedly it was an out of control drug scene, but it was still only part of the whole experience of being a member of the Casino and the northern soul scene in general. There was also the travelling to get there to be a part of it. The friendliness of being in such an infectious cult minority. The love of the music and the dancing. They could have done it real justice, and reported on all these aspects of Wigan Casino, as the documentary from Granada did, but in the true spirit of tabloid journalism, they fucked all over what was happening and caused many a parent versus offspring Sunday afternoon row as the family tucked into the roast beef, Yorkshire pudding and vegetables.

For a scene that usually shunned publicity in any form, it felt like we had overdosed on it. Even *Top Of The Pops* gave coverage to the music by inviting various Casino regulars to appear on the programme, wearing the obligatory soulie uniform of wide bags, flat soled leather shoes, cord bomber jackets and star jumpers, to go through their energetic routines to the strains of *Footsee* and *Skiing In The Snow*. There they were on *Top Of The Pops* spinning, back-dropping and splitting to a northern track that immediately went out of favour among northern fans the day it appeared on the programme. This over-publicity didn't really do the reputation of the Casino much good apart from getting the music recognised, but we'd done that already so it all seemed a pointless waste of time.

The glare of the spotlight didn't concentrate on the Casino long enough to wreck it, and it eventually returned to the underground scene it had started out as. The pissheads and the culture vultures came in their coachloads to stick their heads in and see what all the fuss was about, but soon discovered the Casino wasn't their scene. It took effort to be a regular on the scene. You had to want to be there and it didn't offer you anything unless you put something, even everything, into it.

Those who came in search of Sharon and Gary were soon fucked off. There were no girls in tight white mini-skirts dancing around their hand bags. No males wearing medallions and jackets with the sleeves rolled up, waiting to make the move that would ensure they'd be on the end of a quick shag or blow job at the end of the evening. Sure they came, but they didn't conquer, and best of all, they soon fucked off and never returned as soon as the realisation hit them that they were well and truly out of their depth. For them it was back to the softer, more acceptable face of clubland where they could play at being kings and queens of the night.

Of more concern and danger to us as the northern scene exploded was divisions within the scene which were played out in the two music mags of the day that catered for all us soul freaks out there. *Blues And Soul,* which is still going as strong today as it was then, and *Black Music.* It became part of the weekend experience, getting *Blues And Soul.* Go into town, buy a few sounds and then down to Smiths' to pick up your copy to read over coffee in Selfridges while trying to look ultra cool for the girls.

Blues And Soul catered for all forms of black and soul music from northern to gospel, from jazz through to African, but there was still a huge gap waiting to be filled music mag-wise, and it was *Black Music* that did the business with some great in-depth reports on the northern scene. It was the brainchild of a guy called Tony Cummings who saw the potential that the northern scene had, and quickly aimed his mag towards the scene. It featured in depth articles, northern soul record charts, and advertisements for northern outlets so we could order the sounds we needed if we couldn't get our hands on them in our local shops.

Since the magazine aimed to review the northern scene fully, it had to recruit the top names associated with the scene and it did just that. It got them all contributing in some way or another, from The Highland Room, Wigan Casino and further back to The Twisted Wheel and The Torch. The very best names from the very best venues gave *Black Music* the credibility among northern freaks it was after.

Ian Levine fronted a regular column called 'Hey - Mr DJ' in which he reviewed the scene in general as well as pushing his own tastes in northern soul to the public. And Dave Godin, a great crusader for the

70

scene and the man who first came up with the phrase "northern soul", had a regular column in which he visited and reported from all the top venues in a punchy, often humorous style. In one issue he said that he really enjoyed his visit to Wigan Casino very much, apart from the lethally slippery toilet floor. Still you can't have everything. Other names on the *Black Music* team were Russ Winstanley (Wigan Casino), his wingman Richard Searling, Soul Sam, Pep, Kev Roberts, John Vincent, Allan Rhodes and ex-Twisted Wheel man, Les Cockell. All of these and more contributed to making *Black Music* a good read for all involved on the northern scene as it flourished during the mid-Seventies.

But over the months, the scene we all loved slowly started to break up. Not wholly, but in the sense of a Blackpool Mecca versus Wigan Casino stance. All manner of arguments were raised in articles that did nothing for the scene except split it up into two rival camps. You were either Mecca or you were Wigan, and that was a shit one from where we were stood. Both venues had a right to their place on the scene and it was wrong to set them against each other. It wasn't as if there were loads of venues you could travel to and listen to northern soul, so why split the scene apart? Anyway, it happened and a battle began between the Highland Room and Wigan Casino.

Wigan was a relative newcomer to the scene, while the Highland Room was a well respected established venue and famed for the quality of soul it played there. In a way it was a club for the purists on the scene who wanted to hear nothing but rare original sounds blasting out from the speakers, as opposed to the cheaper widely available bootleg copies that were played at other venues. A fact that it made crystal clear as Wigan Casino began its rise to the top spot.

Tony Cummings visited The Highland Room for a night and then described its clientele as the true connoisseurs of the northern soul scene. It also said that the scene at the Casino was an inferior one, with its clientele being described as, "The black bombing bootleg playing dull brained brothers from Wigan".

It was a clear dig at Wigan, insinuating that all they did there was listen to cheap bootleg copies while out of their skulls on speed. Not so Mr Cummings. You never did have much time for the Casino though.

Okay, there were a fair number of bootleg sounds knocking about at the Casino, but the disc jockeys didn't limit themselves to playing them. And what Wigan did with its music policy was bold and upfront. It broke down all the elitism and the mystery that went hand in hand with the original northern sounds of the day. It made the sounds accessible to the people that mattered. Those out on the dancefloor who kept coming back week after week to get more of what the Wigan jocks were playing.

In addition to Levine's policy of spinning only rare original sounds, the Highland Room also adopted a black soul music only policy that was praised by the one and only Tony Cummings who was well in favour of the "no white soul stompers allowed" attitude. Apparently the only true and credible soul we should have been switched on to was black soul. What a load of shit that was. I mean we all know black soul is special, but some great stuff came from white soul artists and such an attitude should never have been suggested by those who knew better. In effect, it was a sly attempt to shit all over the Casino and its jockeys and the brilliant scene they had created there. A scene that was now growing at a fantastic pace as each week passed by.

It became a constant battle between the two venues as each magazine issue put forward contrasting viewpoints. One week the Highland Room would win hands down, and the next, Wigan Casino would top out. But all through the aggro, the Highland Room was fighting a losing battle as the Casino membership just got bigger and bigger.

Once again it turned its fire on the type of "soulie" the Casino attracted, or so it thought, in the September '75 issue of *Black Music*. Funnily enough, just after Tommy Hunt's brilliant live appearance on the Casino stage to celebrate the club's second anniversary. What a storming night that turned out to be. The articles once again referred to the drug scene at the club and the playing of white soul. A thing the Highland Room would never stoop to, putting their ever so precious clientele through the pain of having to listen to white soul.

One of the lines read "rail workers from Crewe, packers from Preston, steel workers from Sheffield and factory hands from Burnley". The article had clear suggestions that the Highland Room was some sort of hallowed upper class northern soul centre of study where only the privileged could graduate, under the ever watchful eye of the learned professor Levine.

And still the slanging match continued with another article slagging off the Casino, but by this time, it was turning out to be second-hand jealousy. And then Russ Winstanley came out of his corner fighting with a comment that hit the nail right on the head. "We are not going pop music at the Casino, but we are determined to keep playing the fast type of northern soul that northern soul has always been about. It's places like the Mecca in Blackpool that are selling out. They are playing the slower funkier type of records which are not true northern soul".

The article ended with, "We are trying to keep the northern scene truly northern" and that about summed up what the Casino was trying to do. Northern wasn't about smooth, funky, slow soul. It was about fast one hundred mile an hour dance music that you could get off on without thinking about it. Just get out on the floor and slide into it and that was that for three minutes. Ian Levine went off on a singular pursuit of a different type of sound with a slower funkier Seventies feel to it that wasn't essentially northern soul, but through all this, he still managed to dig up the occasional gem of a sound reminiscent of the old days in the Highland Room.

1975, saw the big split between the two venues and Ian Levine's words went as follows: "Half the kids follow Wigan and the stomp stomp dancers, some of which are pop music, and half follow the Mecca and are into rare uptempo strictly black soul". The media had well and truly succeeded in splitting the northern scene down the middle, and for many of us, had helped to destroy many of the good memories shared up in the Highland Room. By then, we were solidly Wigan Casino. The scene just could not be beaten in any way. Somewhere along the way, Levine had lost his winning formula and pursued his own path, and it's sad to think that the room that once played class northern ended its days playing smooth sounds that failed to come close to the top sounds that used to blast out from the speakers there.

The Highland Room eventually died a death and closed another chapter in northern soul history. And what of Levine? He became a top producer in the States producing high energy music, doing very well for himself indeed. And he's had a large part in the production of Gloria Estefan's latest effort, bringing more than a touch of the old northern feeling to her work.

The Casino had won a bitter war to be the number one venue on the scene, and it was a title it never relinquished during the time it remained open. With all that nasty media inspired slanging out of the way, we could settle down and get back to enjoying ourselves at Wigan, but the nights in the Highland Room will never be forgotten, and its place in northern soul history is assured forever.

One positive aspect of all the publicity and hype was to bring Wigan Casino to the attention of the record labels Stateside, who then sent many legendary stars of soul over the Atlantic to perform. Junior Walker, Martha Reeves, The Marvellettes, Jackie Wilson and Edwin Starr all appeared in the hallowed main hall and were bowled over by the special atmosphere generated by the dedicated and informed Wigan audience. The very best soul artists came to pay homage in the temple of soul, a fact readily endorsed by the American music magazine, *Billboard*, which voted Wigan Casino the world's best soul venue.

The world's best soul venue. Suck on that one Sunday tabloids. That's how special Wigan Casino was. It demanded the best and it got the best. The night Edwin Starr came to the Casino was one of the best experiences anyone who was a member of the club could have had. He's still doing the rounds these days and bangs out the music as good and as loud as he always has done, but back in the early Seventies, Edwin Starr was truly in his prime. A monster in the music industry and top of the tree.

It was a scoop that the Casino management had booked him to perform in the club, and the buzz weeks before he appeared was incredible. Just about everybody was going to that one for sure. The night before, we were all down at Blackpool Casino sorting out the gear and who was taking who. Making sure nobody was left out in the cold for the big night. The crew had hired a van, so Saturday night saw us packed into a transit with all the main faces on the scene. Some we'd known since school, and others had become close friends through being regulars at the Casino in Blackpool. Mick McLaughlin, Ged Grennell, Johnny Walsh, Roy Koniecek, Mark Eyre, Daz Hall, Mitch, Bob Blackwood, Andy Pape and all the other heads that were there and part of the northern soul scene.

Soon we were steaming down the M6 nice and early to make sure we all got in since the night was going to be a biggie for sure. The van was full of marijuana, the sounds were belting out from the speakers, and all was cool. The short journey down to the Casino was spent sharing out cans of beer, wraps of speed and joints, and we soon forgot about the numb arses and being crushed together as we left the M6 and pulled up outside the Casino.

A couple of beers in a Wigan pub and it was time to join the massive queue already waiting for the doors to open. People seemed to be appearing from everywhere in an attempt to see the man himself. The queue that night was an absolute fucker, and we were wedged in a good hour and a half before the doors were opened. When opening time came, we literally had to be pulled in by the bouncers.

The buzz in the main hall was electric as we all settled into a few sounds before Edwin took to the stage. The place was alive and jam packed with heads waiting for the big moment. Gerry Marshall appeared on stage with microphone in hand and announced to us all that Mr Edwin Starr was about to appear and would we give a massive round of applause for one of the great soul legends of Tamla Motown. The crowd moved en masse to the front of the stage after the thunderous reception, to which the immaculately dressed, white-suited Edwin Starr bounced on stage with his full backing band.

We were only a few feet away from the man as he shouted, "Good evening Wigan Casino!", and then immediately ripped into a storming set of soul. The whole of the main hall from floor to balcony was moving to the music he was belting out, and Mr Starr really looked to be thoroughly enjoying the Wigan experience to the full. Everyone was dancing, clapping and singing along to every song he came out with. It was an upfront one hundred per cent performance in front of an audience that knew his stuff inside out, and he soon realised that to turn in anything less than a perfect performance would be an insult to the Wigan regulars.

Everyone had come to see a Motown legend do his thing, and what a thing he did that night. He went through all the much loved classics with a passion and energy second to none, and he brought the house down with *War*, *Headline News*, and the brilliant *25 Miles*. By then he knew he had the whole crowd absolutely behind him, as we all danced and clapped our way through his set. By the end of the second encore, we were all covered in sweat. Edwin Starr had proved beyond any shadow of doubt that he was more than worthy of the tremendous live reputation he'd come by, and he left us all breathless and exhausted. It was a case of you had to be there to fully experience the buzz of that all nighter.

We all came off the dancefloor soaked in sweat and exhausted, and everyone just crashed out. In the Blackpool corner, we sat around talking or getting into a couple of cold Cokes and a joint to bring us back to reality. It had all been too much, but having said that, there was still an all nighter to go at and get through, so after a change of clothes and a couple of bombers, we were once again ready for the business at hand. The all nighter seemed to fly by, and it wasn't long before we were once again crushed into the van, complete with numb arses, and on the way back to boring Blackpool. Smoking and shivering our way back to reality once again.

The drug or gear scene was an integral part of the Casino experience for so many regulars. Traditionally, the northern scene had always had a strong connection with drugs, stretching back to the days of The Torch and Twisted Wheel in Manchester. The Casino just followed on in that tradition of speed-fuelled all nighters. The nature of the scene created the opening for the use of drugs, and dropping gear just became something you did. The final ingredient in the Wigan recipe, there for all who wanted to sample it. It was a youthful underground scene that shunned alcohol, so something was needed to fill the gap. To most Casino goers, the all nighter just wasn't the same without a couple of bombers or a wrap of whizz inside them.

As we became familiar faces on the scene, we soon got to know the score. What to touch and vice versa, and all the people we knew who dropped gear regularly seemed okay on it. None of them having a bad time or experiencing the kind of horror shows you could get with acid. The only side effects with speed was the coming down. Nothing too painful, but you'd get a prickly feeling inside you for a couple of days as your body and mind adjusted to sleeping again after the surge of energy the speed gave you. You'd be short tempered and restless, but nothing too manic.

Amphetamine was the drug everybody dropped. Speed, whizz or gear. It was readily available in huge quantities and ridiculously cheap for what you got out of it when you were on a full flyer. You never spewed your guts up on gear, unless you'd done loads, and you never ended up kicking some poor fucker's head in just because he happened to talk a little differently to you. You were in control, and all you felt was this tremendous rush of confidence and energy that would stay with you for hours, days even, if you had taken too much.

It came in pill, capsule and powder form in a multitude of colours. Like millions of Smarties that were only suitable for grown ups who went to the Casino. The market for gear was massive, and the dealers found it well difficult to meet the demand at times. The ones we knew back in Blackpool were okay. A little slippery, but that was sort of acceptable. The occasional deal was a little on the thin side, but that was part of the game and some gear was better than no gear. If they took the piss too much, they'd simply get a good stomping and we'd find other dealers who could supply us with top gear. But even if the deal was a little thin, it was better than buying from the lowlife

76

scumbags who sold stuff that had been tampered with. Cut with a substitute powder so they could increase their profits.

They would use flour, glucose, sugar crushed up, and even talcum powder in their attempts to get extra cash. Mix it in with some strong whizz and people would never tell. It was a shit low-life trick, but even lower were the dealers who thought they'd have a laugh and mix a bit of Vim in there, and with a wrap of that shit inside you, you were in trouble. Real painful trouble that lasted hours. Intense headaches, vomiting, stomach cramps. The full horror show, and by the time it wore off you'd spewed the lot out of your system.

It was big business in the early to mid Seventies, and to keep up with the demand the dealers turned to the places they knew contained drugs in the amounts they needed. The good old high street chemist shop. They hit these with a vengeance and knew exactly where to look once inside the shop. In minutes they'd be in, would break open the dangerous drugs cabinet, and be on their way with jars full of drugs to sell to their clients waiting patiently back in the pubs. To some of them it was that simple. In the time it took somebody to sink a pint of beer, they had located the chemist, got in, got the drugs out of the cabinet, and were back in the pub, screwing the lid off the big brown jars and telling their cronies to help themselves. The word would be out. A crowd would gather and the necessary silver would cross palms, and that would be that until the next time.

Amphetamine powder was the one most widely available. The guy we used was cool and used to buy it pure, so we were always sure of a clean deal, but the big minus with phet was the smell and taste. Like cat piss, but the more it made you want to heave, the better the deal, so it was grin and bear it time. A deep breath. Get it in your mouth and swallow it down with a beer or a Coke and wait until it worked on you, which was usually about fifteen minutes. You could snort it through a nice crispy rolled up fiver but eating it was easier. Nothing worse than your nose dribbling amphet powder all over the place. Ten minutes after doing a wrap you'd be at it. On the dancefloor and giving it your best. And it was cheap at three to five quid a wrap.

If you were wedged up, you could go luxury and sort some coke out. Well expensive and short-lived compared to amphet, but it was smooth beyond belief. Mix it up with a bit of amphet powder and it would last out a bit longer, but the best way to do it was to buy bulk with a mob of you and everyone would end up with a nice fat wrap. You could get in deep with cocaine though and before you realised it, you'd be drowning.

77

There were some nasty pills around called chalksticks. Do too many of those and your stomach lining would take a battering, but again, they were cheap. Even cheaper than powder and a last resort at Wigan if all the sources had dried up. I tried them the one time and they were strong. Half a dozen nearly blew my head off, but it was the one and only time. Figured I needed my stomach lining more than I needed a headful of chalkies, but a lot of other people got off on them.

There were also blueys. Dexedrine, more commonly known as Dexy's Midnight Runners. Three quid would get you an awesome handful of these little powerhouses and with those inside you, your all nighter would really go with a buzz. We all liked blueys. A good standby if you couldn't find the best stuff, as they were strong and cheap. Every so often, the market would be flooded with home made back street blueys, and these were just as strong, if not stronger than the originals, so they were always a sound bet.

A little bit more upmarket and you could get your hands on better gear. Green and clears. Filon. And the gear so many of the Casino regulars rated. The black bomber. The creme de la creme of the gear scene, and these really did do the business to your metabolism. And virtually no come down either. No sleep whatsoever, but no pricklies or stomach cramps so one out of three isn't too bad. They were really strong and we never did more than half a dozen on an all nighter. The big plus with bombers was that they were virtually tamper proof. If the thin purple band around the middle of the capsule had been removed, then you wouldn't entertain it at all. It had obviously been split open and the powder removed and substituted with flour or similar. If you did them constantly, you would build up a resistance to them and needed more to get you up there each week, so the trick was to lay off them for a couple of all nighters and hit them again, or mix them up with an assortment of gear. An all nighter cocktail.

A few of the mob mixed up speed with acid, but most stayed with speed. No telling what acid would do to you if you were up on the balcony and you decided to do one over the top. Speed was never weird, just the business. A gradual build up of energy and elation that stayed in you for hours as it raced around your insides. It gave you bags of self confidence too. More than enough to pull Miss World if she had been out on that dancefloor, but she never turned up. Not even for one all nighter. It stripped you of all inhibitions and made you feel totally at ease with your surroundings and the people that came up to you. It was unbeatable that feeling, when the sounds were blasting out, you were on the dancefloor, and into a warp factor six deep sea rave. Nothing else in the world mattered because you were at the very centre of the world and that was that.

I'd done a few all nighters at the Casino before deciding to drop some gear. I remember being a little scared at the time, but thought what the fuck. My mate handed me a couple of the magical black cylinders and I popped them down my throat and swallowed them with a mouthful of Coke. I then just sat there in the corner waiting for the fireworks to begin. It was a jam packed Casino that night and I was full of it. Sweat and anticipation as I waited to come up, but I didn't need to wait all that long for the bombers to start work on me. Within ten minutes they'd hit me, and were racing around my bloodstream like a train. No head trips or horror shows. Just sweat and energy and this build up of total confidence inside me. It was fucking brilliant and that all nighter flew by like no tomorrow. I danced, talked and ran around the Casino like a madman for the whole night, and in what seemed like no time at all, I was heading down the stairs with my all nighter bag on my shoulders, my shades on, and still full of it. Got back to Blackpool and chilled out in a coffee bar we all used and wondered where the fuck the last eight hours of my life had gone to. Just incredible those two bombers, and I must have drank twenty cups of coffee that day as I sat and talked and talked and listened to some jukebox sounds. Any jukebox sounds so long as there was some noise in the background to fill in the gaps the conversation didn't.

That first all nighter on gear was memorable for another reason, and a frightening one at the time. I fought my way through to the toilets, sweat pouring out of me and my heart pounding away, and eventually found a cubicle where I discovered one of the side effects speed has on the body, or one part of the body. I was bursting so I unzipped my trousers and searched for my dick. And to my horror I found that it had shrunk. And had it shrunk. *Fuck me*, I thought. *What am I going to do now with a dick this size*. Thankfully it was only a temporary side effect, but nobody told me this would happen and I just didn't bother to ask. Not something you think about, but that night in those toilets it scared the shit out of me for a time.

The toilets inside the Casino were a fucking disaster area and a main dealing place as well. Not a pleasant experience going into the toilets with leaking water running down the walls, and always half an inch of water mixed with piss covering the floor. And if you were wearing anything white, then you had to extra careful. So many guys smoked in there that the nicotine used to rise up to the ceiling, mix with the condensation and drip, drip, drip, all over you. A dirty brown liquid that looked even better on the dancefloor under the ultra violet light.

The toilets were always packed to capacity with people changing, waiting to have a crap or dropping their gear before they hit the main hall for the night. And always a team of muscled up black guys doing the top dealing. They looked handy and you'd have to think twice about having a go at them, but there was no need because they were cool and there for the same reasons as we were. Scoring some gear. It would all be concluded in minutes. A handshake, a nod and a brief conversation. What was on offer and how much. Money would be exchanged and you'd get a little package in your hands from one of them who winked and shook hands, and you'd be off to drop it. And they'd be there in the same place if you were running a bit low on energy and needed a top up. Rare but it did happen and even though it was a bit intimidating, like a bottle tester fronting up to the black guys, the gear they sold was top class and once your face became known, they were cool with you.

When the Casino hit the headlines and attracted all sorts of attention from culture vultures through to the drug squad, you didn't know who the fuck was who, and the gear became scarce. Underground and very expensive, with little dealing going on inside the place. You'd sort it before you got to Wigan so as to make sure you'd have a good one. By then, most of the faces I knew were well into the gear, and to attempt an all nighter without the final ingredient would be an unthinkable idea. So you either got sorted or you didn't go.

There was never any of that peer pressure shit at Wigan. You either did gear or you didn't and that was enough. It was an out of control aspect to the all night scene and it just added another dimension to an already enjoyable experience. There were people who remained straight throughout their time at the Casino and every credit to them for doing that. But the vast majority of Casino-goers dropped gear. For some it was purely a tool for enjoyment. Get back to tinseltown and remain straight for the week and get at it again at the weekend. But for others, the need turned into a necessity, and their habit slowly took over them. Their original motive for being at the Casino, which was the music, took a second place to their personal needs.

Most of the people we knew on the scene, those who had been doing the all nighters for a few years, were up to twenty to thirty pills or capsules or wraps a weekend. A serious intake of drugs, and a few even took it further and cranked their gear - injecting it into themselves so that the hit would be a fast one. We even thought about it for a time, but we somehow managed to keep a grip on reality. Cranking was the next stop before the end of the line. We even swore to go straight a number of times. Do an all nighter without using gear and mean it. But it was useless. We'd be there at a packed night and your mates would be wide eyed and full of it, and we'd be as flat as a dead battery in winter. All the solemn vows went out of the window and somebody would produce a couple of bombers or a nice fat wrap of whizz, and we'd be off again on the amphetamine roller coaster. And a better roller coaster than you could ever find in Blackpool.

And through all this seedy world of wheeling and dealing we had to be continually on our toes in case the plod appeared in search of drugs. The possibility of getting busted was a distant one, but it was still there and we had to look out for it in case it was our turn for the big one. Getting a conviction for drugs along with a fine was something nobody looked forward to. Not even the hardened druggies who only really cared where the next hit was coming from.

The plod operated in the pubs and clubs of Blackpool in an attempt to remove the dealers from the street. But as soon as one had been busted, in stepped another to replace him. A lot of them figured that a bust and a short spell in the nick was worth the risk because the profit and business they were doing was never ending. The first time would be a large fine, but they had the cash to sort that one out. Second time maybe a period inside or probation, but they'd be out in a few months so what the fuck. Most of them saw nick as an inconvenience. A break in their business empire and nothing more. But a dealer who'd been away from a fast moving ever changing market could find it tough to get his name around again once he was out. Others simply stepped in to cream the business, and sometimes the only way to get back into it was to resort to violence. Take the newcomer out and give him a fucking good going over and that happened many times. The old dealer was back in business and his wallet started to get fat again.

The late night trains were popular places from which to deal gear. They operated on them, selling their gear to anybody who wanted it, while little old ladies sat writing postcards and reflected on their day trip to Blackpool. Totally oblivious to what was going on around them. Eventually the news that the trains were a hotbed of illicit dealing got back to the boys in blue so they decided to do something about it. Couldn't have innocent passengers being terrorised by these drug taking late night fiends. So between stations they would stage impromptu visits and search everybody they thought looked like a soulie. And some they won and some they lost, as the word spread among us that plod were on the case and looking for arses to bust.

One particular evening we were on the last train to Wigan and everyone was having a kicking time. The beer was flowing, the music was blasting out from a portable, and the joints were being passed around with a vengeance. Talk was about this and that and what the all nighter would be like. Even though we'd done it a hundred times and knew exactly what it was going to be like, each one felt different. The gear, the late night travel and meeting up with people you only saw once a week kept the buzz well and truly alive. A couple of guys were knocking out the gear and were doing a roaring trade but for this all nighter, we had our stuff sorted out the night before. The train pulled into Preston and waited the usual ten minutes. People getting off and people getting on. Guards checking tickets and so on and so on. Suddenly a mob of plod arrived and started to board the train en masse. A peak capped officer tells everyone to remain in their seats while police officers search for drugs. Talk about head-doing. Caught on a train with the plod crawling all over it, and about to get a pull for sure. Initial panic set in as we looked at each other, thinking just what the fuck are we going to do now. The plod were moving up the carriages at an alarming rate, going through all nighter bags, seriously looking for the slightest traces of gear. In minutes they'd be on us and that would be that. Goodnight Vienna and a night in the cells, followed by a charge and an appearance in court. It was time for some fast thinking. Two close mates, Molaf and Johnny who did many all nighters with me and Ged, suddenly came out with a move that even George Best, playing to a packed Old Trafford, would have applauded.

Luckily for us that night, we'd brought along some food in case we got an attack of the hungers. A few packets of crisps and a couple of Burton's meat and potato pies. They were the tops in pies and if you were into pies, then Burton's were the ones to be seen eating. Just as the movement of drawing breath was starting to become very difficult, Mick goes into the bag and takes out the pies. Takes the pastry tops off. Scoops out some of the delicious filling, puts two bags of equally delicious gear into the pies and presses the tops back on. He puts them back into the bag and we all slip into silence as the plod arrive with smiling faces, asking us to turn out the contents of our bags for a search. Talking to us in that semi-official condescending tone they like to address members of the public in. We obliged and handed them our bags, one after another, so they could give them the once over and get the fuck out of it.

It was prickly stuff that night as they pulled out our clothes, deodorant sprays, towels and the Burton's pies with a look of "Now what have we got 'ere, then?". One of the inquisitive plods said, "These look good, lads", and put the pies back in the bag and returned them to our sportsbags. He never knew just how good those pies were.

A series of friendly questions followed. "How long had we been going to the Casino?" "What is northern soul all about?" And "did we ever take drugs?"

"About two years officer, and northern soul is just another type of soul music, and of course we didn't take drugs, officer. What do you think we are?"

I brought into the conversation the fact that my old man was an ex-copper and he'd kill me if I even looked at a drug, and that had the desired effect on the plod. He left us with a "Have a good night, lads".

And we certainly did, thanks to our little friends in the Burton's pies.

That night was the closest we, as the gang of four, came to being nicked in a big way. But an incident happened to me that cut closer to the bone outside the Casino one evening. An evening that began with a loud hailered verbal warning from a peak cap plod to the large crowd gathered on the street outside the club. It was absolutely pissing down. Wind and rain everywhere and totally miserable, so we were huddled under the canopy in an attempt to keep dry. The peak cap continued to shout his displeasure about us blocking the pavement and wanted us all to disperse so people could get past. It wasn't exactly the busiest street in England at half past midnight, so we stayed our ground and shouted back a few humorous comments that fell on uniformed deaf ears.

He ordered his officers in to disperse the crowd and instantly I knew my number was up when a fine example of a burly British bobby grabbed me and hauled me over to a waiting transit van, and threw me in the back where several other unfortunate soulies were sitting, looking extremely fucked off by what was happening. I was put at the back of the van, next to the doors and well out of view of the officers sat in the front seat who kept throwing us looks that said just wait until we get you fuckers down to the nick. Then we will have some fun.

Thankfully, they weren't the most alert members of Wigan Constabulary and I realised it was a now or never situation to get rid of the two grammes of whizz I had in my coat pocket. Once at the station and the searching started, I'd be a gonna for sure, so there was nothing else but to do it in the van there and then.

I cautiously moved my hand down to my pocket, picked up the two grammes and made my way up to my mouth with the fat wrap of whizz. A fake cough followed and I swallowed the lot, wrapper and all. The guy sat next to me gave me a friendly nod and a wink, and then did the same. We exchanged a few words about our victory and then it was doors shut and a warp factor drive down to Wigan plod station where we were all searched and then interviewed about the incidents outside the Casino. I managed to keep my answers down to one word when the plod took a statement from me I was buzzing like fuck. Flying higher than a stealth bomber doing the business over Iraq, but I just about convinced them that I was a. law abiding citizen most of the time. They kept us all for a couple of hours, in an attempt to fuck up our all nighter, but they eventually let us go and we ran up to the Casino like lightning. And that was the end of a potentially damaging incident that would have meant the end of my all nighter life if they'd had busted me for possessing whizz. A close one!

Some people inevitably took their habits to the extremes and paid the price. Sadly this was the case with several people we knew well, and who got into gear in a big way and couldn't find a way out of it all. Friends who gradually deteriorated from strong, healthy people into weak willed, do anything for a buzz, ghostly looking shadows. Theirs was a slow desperate decline into a nightmare world of painful unreality, with their habit taking over as the prime reason for living. People like Phil Booth who went from number one style guru to looking like death in search of fresh veins to inject the shit into his body. Ten minutes after a crank and the old Phil would surface once again and he'd return to the top spot for a time. Later he'd be in agony - until the next shot of relief. And Daz Hall, another friend who slipped into the dirty desperate world of day to day drug taking that eventually killed him. He even resorted to robbing and beating up friends, but by then, Daz was in another world entirely. Beyond all reasoning as he became one of the army of crankers' strongest recruits.

An incident involving Daz, shortly before he died, brought home to us just how deep we were into the gear scene. It screamed to us to get the fuck out of all this while we still had a chance to get out. Ged and I were in the car park one freezing cold early morning outside the Casino. The Blackpool soul mob had hired a van for the night and mid way through the all nighter, we decided to take a breather and go across to the van for a rest. It was five in the morning and misty, dark and icy cold. A real fucker of a Wigan morning and the two of us rushed across the car park to get into the van for our sheepskins and a bit of shut eye.

We jumped in the back and were surprised to see Daz in there with several crazy looking deadbeats. Real low life specimens who looked like they'd have you over at a second's notice. Thin and dirty looking, with the aura of smackheads all over them. They weren't too pleased at the intrusion and a few words were said, but we weren't going anywhere. We'd paid for the van after all, so it was a case of if you don't like it, then get the fuck out of it and leave us alone.

Daz sensed the tense atmosphere in the van and tried to lighten it with introductions and a joke or two, but he failed miserably. Some heads you dislike instantly, no matter how many times they shake your hand and ask you what you do for a living and all the usual introductory bullshit. And these guys were the bottom of the barrel and couldn't say anything to change our opinion of them.

We pulled our sheepskins on and snuggled into them. Hands in pockets and collars up so we could get warm. The atmosphere in the van was one of total sadness and desperation huddled together, as droplets of condensation dripped from the roof to annoy you every so often.

We watched them go through their tragic ritual of getting a hit. Tying cords around their arms to pump up what was left of their veins, while Daz sorted out the syringe, filling it with gear and making sure there were no airlocks to cause them trouble. It was murky looking stuff, but he reckoned it was top class stuff that would knock their heads off. I remember looking at Ged and thinking it was time to call it a day. Not just for what we were witnessing in the van. That was scary enough, but the whole scene we had become submerged in. It all seemed so sick and seedy from where we were sat that early morning.

There were six or seven of them with one needle between them. Daz made a joke about the needle being a bit on the blunt side, and laughed about it still doing the trick if they jabbed it in hard enough. He kicked off the proceedings, followed by all the others in turn, and we watched in silence as the gear hit them and they changed into talkative lively guys who left us to it as the sudden surge of energy told them it was time to get back on the dancefloor again. The last guy was pissed off that the needle was blunt and he really jabbed it into his arm as Daz laughed manically. It brought home to us that Daz was well on his way out and that we'd be joining him if we weren't careful. After all, he'd started on blow and speed as we'd done, and ended up on all sorts of shit. We both left the van feeling pretty sick and deeply disturbed, but it had been the best lesson we could have wished to have had during that particular period of our lives. No more warnings were necessary.

A few hours later on that same morning, we were heading home in the van with Daz and his cranking cronies. He'd promised them a lift home to wherever they lived, but that wasn't on. We were all pretty fucked and coming down in a big way, so we said we'd drop them off at the Tickled Trout and they could get home from there. We were heading into Preston when, all of a sudden, one of the druggies went into a wild crazy fit and began thrashing around and vomiting all over the place. The coming down was bad enough, but when someone is spewing up and having a fit, it gets too much. We pulled over to the side of the road, but by then, the guy had passed out, covered in this foul smelling sick. We tried to bring him round, but there was no chance. He was out of it. All facial colour gone and nobody, not even the other crankers, knew who the fuck he was or where he lived. It was a splendid situation to be in.

We were starving hungry, it was freezing cold, and we had little to no petrol left to get home. It was like that some mornings. All of us pissed off and skint, but we always made it back to base. Someone pointed out that petrol was low and there was no money so we couldn't fuck about wasting time on driving around Lancashire trying to find out where he lived. So we got him out of the van and carried him over to a grass verge and laid him out on the ground. That way he'd be spotted for sure and taken to hospital, or we could alert the authorities when we got back to Blackpool and they could take it from there. It's like the guy could have been dying, but all that concerned us was getting home to our beds and a nice cup of tea to warm us up. He was laid out in the ditch like some vampire waiting for the night. Somebody threw his sportsbag out of the van, we all jumped in, shut the doors and started the van up. First gear, a rev on the pedal and that was that. Off and out of it and back to Blackpool without a care in the world.

Nobody batted an eyelid or gave a fuck about the poor bloke or where we'd dumped him. Somebody would find him lying there in the ditch for sure, or that's what we kept telling ourselves on the way back to tinseltown. By the time we actually arrived home I doubt if anybody remembered what we'd done not an hour before. We kept a keen interest in the news over the next couple of weeks to see if anything appeared about the incident, but there was nothing so we assumed he woke up and made his way home. After that appalling incident, we didn't need telling that the emotionally cold situation we were locked into was getting well out of control.

Taking gear in the amounts we were swallowing it, over the length of time we'd been regulars at the Casino, wasn't any good at all. Speed gets you but not in the sense heroin gets you. Heroin gets you and fucks all over you, and you either get your head around the problem and try to get off it, or you end up six foot under. But with speed it's different. It gradually drags you into a world where everything appears to be totally unreal, and serious real life situations suddenly don't seem all that serious anymore. You lose a lot of weight but you don't think you do, a fact that was brought home to me one night when somebody showed me a picture of myself taken in the Casino. Stood in the Blackpool corner, wide eyed and crazy looking, my rib cage was there for all to see. I looked like something off David Bowie's *Diamond Dogs* album cover, and the worst of it was that the photograph had been taken a couple of years previous. I looked like a bag of shit then, so what did I look like now? Pretty good I figured, but judging by the piccie I was looking at, I was well wrong. I was kidding myself that all the chemicals I'd thrown down my neck were having no effect on me whatsoever, and it was time I did something about it. Not just me but all the mob that had done the all nighters as long as I'd done them. That was the reality of it, but it felt like we were all totally cool about the situation. And that was the unreality. No matter how serious the situation appeared to be, we might as well have been living in a Walt Disney cartoon. It not only affected your grip on life, but totally warped it to the point where nothing appeared to be that serious or for that matter stupid.

Like the time we'd missed our lift to the Casino and were flat broke. We were with Phil Booth that evening and all of us desperate to get there somehow. Phil comes out with an absolute amphetamine inspired classic. He decides that it would be cool to take one of the brand new transit vans that were parked outside Thomas Motors, the local Ford dealer where we used to have the dope in the roof adventures. It was common knowledge that the vans were wired up to the plod. Nick one and you'd be caught for sure. They'd be on you like a ton of bricks. But there we were waiting for Phil to break in, which he did in minutes. We settled down in the back of the sparkling new tranny van as Phil tried to hot wire it, and suddenly cops were everywhere. Pulled us out of the van, slapped us around a little, and read us the riot act. Told us all we'd shit our hole full this time, and that we were going to be charged down at the nick.

It was only some neat inspired talking from yours truly that got us off the legal hook. I spun them the yarn about the old man being a well respected ex-plain clothes plod, and anything else I could think of to get the copper on our side. Told him I was sitting my A levels and wanted to join the RAF, and that if I was nicked, then I'd have no chance of flying jets for them. The peaked cap relaxed a bit and gave us a stern warning about the implications if we ever attempted such a stupid thing in the future. My perfectly worded script did the trick, and after another almighty bollocking, he told us to get our arses home. I mean, the plod parked up not fifty yards away from the vans and there we were breaking in to get a lift to the Casino, thinking we'd get away with it. But speed does that. Gives you the false confidence to attempt just about anything no matter how stupid or impossible the task seems.

One night it gave Phil Booth the stamina and confidence to get to the Casino against all odds. We were heading down to Wigan one summer's evening and there was Phil sitting on a bench all on his own. Head in hands and looking well desperate. We pulled over to check if he was cool and he said he needed a lift to Wigan and asked to come with us. The car was already full and we hardly knew the driver, so we couldn't press the point home too much or he might get pissed off. Phil even offered to go in the boot, but the guy was having none of it so we said goodbye to Phil who told us he would get there. He picked up his all nighter bag, slung it over his shoulder and with wide bulging eyes, began walking down the road.

We felt shit about leaving Phil, but the guy driving was a square so we had no choice and soon Phil was out of sight. The next time we saw the thin white duke that all nighter was at four in the morning. Covered in sweat and eyes wider than ever, he had a crazy insane grin all over his face. Told us he'd given up thumbing a lift, had got his head down and walked the whole way to the Casino. And judging by the way he looked, we had no reason to doubt him. He changed into some fresh kit, and was off in a flash to make up for lost time out on the dancefloor.

The one that really drummed home to me just how fucked up I was becoming was late one Friday night, after getting in from Blackpool Casino. Everything had been sorted for the all nighter. The transport, the gear and who was going with who. By that time I was doing heaps of the stuff and thoroughly worn out most of the week, so Friday was an early night so I'd be ready for the Casino. As I came into the flat, I noticed my old man at the top of the stairs, fully dressed and lying in a heap. I thought maybe he's pissed up and couldn't make the stairs, but the old man never touched a drop so that was really out of the question. As I got near him, he was semi-conscious and mumbling to himself about having a heart attack, and asking for a doctor or an ambulance or anything.

The reality of the situation seemed a galaxy away as I stood there looking down at him and thinking is this for real or what. There was a strong possibility of my old man dying in front of me, and I'm doing jack shit about it. It didn't seem all that serious and all I had on my mind was getting up to my pit and getting my head down for a solid eight hours so I'd be fresh for Saturday. The last chance I would have to catch some sleep before the bombers got working on me once again. I viewed the situation as hassle, and hassle I could well do without.

I took the easy option and knocked on my old dear's bedroom door and gave her the news that the old man was about to die on the stairs and could she sort it out. The situation was even more fucked up because for some reason at the time, we were missing a telephone so she pulled on a dressing gown and rushed out to make a call from a nearby public call box. And I just calmly crawled up to my pit, stripped off and dived into bed, thinking of the all nighter and how good it would be.

I woke in the morning after a top sleep to discover that the old dear had sorted it out in fine style, and that he had suffered a slight heart attack. She also told me that he remembered nothing of the night before and about what had happened. I thanked her, jumped in the bath and spent the rest of the day not only thinking about the all nighter, but just how far out I'd gone. But there I was that night, at the Casino with a few bombers in me, doing what I'd done for the last six years.

Everything was becoming really crazy, especially towards the end of the nighters at the Casino. The drug scene was over the moon in the out of control stakes, and we all knew it was only a matter of time before it was taken away from us. It just couldn't go on. People we knew were overdosing regularly, or nearly overdosing. Getting home after an all nighter with eyes wide open and no appetite to speak of for a couple of days, and trying to hold down a job in between all the shit, was becoming harder and harder. And Phil and Daz both ending up on a mortuary slab in less than five years. It was like the Casino was destroying itself, or rather the mass of regulars who attended with unswerving devotion week in, week out. Sometimes it all got too much, trying to keep up with it all and wondering just why the fuck we were there every Saturday.

Cops were everywhere towards the end of it all. Waiting at night for people to nick for carrying gear, and they were there in the morning waiting just as eagerly to nick, nick, nick, and nick them they did. Coming out of an all nighter after you'd danced your arse off and still out of your nut on gear was a sobering experience. The early morning would greet you with a kick up the arse, and it would be on with the shades, bag over your shoulder and off until the next time. People were often confused at this time coming into daylight and still speeding their balls off. Not in the mood for hanging around, they'd be off. Get in the motor, start the engine, get into first gear and off with a whoosh. Straight into somebody's motor, or worse, crash into a garden wall. The plod would arrive and they'd be nicked for sure. Some made a run for it, but it was useless as the car could be traced and they would get it on their return home.

We witnessed many such scenes from the safety of the high rise flats we used whenever we wanted some peace and quiet to chill out. The flats were near the Casino and very high. A good place to get your head down, grab a pint of milk or fresh orange juice off a doorstep, and skin up a nice joint to get rid of the speed flying around in your head. It felt like we were on top of the world some summer nights up there. Up on the roof and watching all the shit going on below us. All the wheeling and dealing going on in the car parks and the corner cafe. People standing all over the place talking, shaking hands and coming to a decision about whether to buy the gear now or wait until something better turned up. Decisions, decisions.

One gorgeous late summer evening we were up on the flats. Ged and I looking down on everything. A real summer's night. Warm, and stars out everywhere adding a real cosmic feel to it all. We cracked open a couple of cat piss amphet and necked it with some milk. We got out the portable Sanyo cassette. Took it up on the roof and stuck some northern on and waited for the whizz to hit us. What a brilliant feeling that night being up there on that roof. Everything felt just right as we messed around for an hour or so, until we were properly flying. I remember going near the edge of the roof and there was no wall or railing or anything to keep you from doing one over the edge. All of a sudden there I am thinking what if I just launch myself off into the blue. Just take a dive and do one to see what would happen. I stood there for about five minutes thinking about it as the gear started to tickle into my imagination department, trying to convince me that I should jump. Would have done no good though. I'd have probably landed on all fours, straight into a backdrop, got up and finished with a spin to end all spins. It was a well weird feeling on that roof that night.

Towards the end, the shortage of gear, and more importantly the lack of good gear, made everybody a little tense. Even nasty, if the gear you'd bought from some face you'd never seen before turned out to be a pile of shit. That would kill your all nighter dead and you'd be out on the car park looking for the guy to try and get your cash back, but he'd be long gone by then. People were getting ripped off inside too, something that never happened before top class gear became rarer and rarer. It was either sort it out in Blackpool beforehand, or take a chance on buying a pocketful of crap. Sometimes if that happened, you'd get lucky and catch the dealer in the cafe. Take him outside and kick fuck out of him until he'd had enough. Other times you'd be unlucky and fast asleep in the corner by the time three in the morning came round. You would have to be extra careful if you were carrying good gear for fear of getting it nicked. If friends were having a bad run, then we'd do the business in tinseltown and they would buy the gear at the price we'd paid for it. Nothing more and nothing less. Just a favour.

One such night we had a classic. A real bad nightmare when Wigan gear was just non-existent. We were sorted and let our friends have their usual stuff bought in Blackpool the night before. It was always a downer when good gear was scarce. The vibe was always one of despair, and people became tense as they realised their all nighter was not going to be the one they'd hoped it would be. That night Ged and I came out of the cafe after dropping off supplies and decided we needed a piss. A narrow alleyway led up one side of the Casino so we thought it would be cool to grab one in there.

We didn't realise it, but as we came out of the cafe and word then spread we had some class gear on us, a team of tough looking black guys hooked onto us, and waited to see what we were up to in the alley. They picked the right time to have us over. Just as were in full flow with our hands full, they blocked off both ends of the alleyway and approached us. One of them with a knife and the other with an empty syringe. Told us both not to make a move or they'd sort us out. Told us to give them all the gear we had on us or we'd end up stabbed. We finished having our piss and thought better of the situation, as there were a good dozen of them and only two of us. Never forget that bastard's grinning face as he looked at our gear and handed it to one of his cronies who then made off with it, and what a shit all nighter that turned out to be.

That incident wasn't the sole reason, but shortly after that we both quit the all nighters. We didn't like what was happening to the scene that had kept us going back for more over a six year period, so we walked out on it. Back to normality and a life in tinseltown. And we coped well with the life as the weeks went by. It was still the hectic place it had always been, and full of the old predictabilia, but we had to quit while we were still one step ahead. It felt weird not to be making all the arrangements. Sorting out the lifts, the gear and who was going with who that night. Going down in Andy's big old Rover and meeting Pete, Rod and Beenie in the corner after they'd returned from some fuck off voyage. And not just them, but all the faces that lived in the Blackpool corner in the Casino.

The memories of all those all nighters burned deep into our souls and one night it all got too much, so we decided to go back one last time to see it, then quit for good. We were at a loose end socially, so one more time wouldn't do us any harm. This was only a couple of months before the Casino closed down for good, but we didn't know that at the time. We just wanted to do it one more time and see for ourselves the rumours that were circulating that the club was no longer the place we loved. Coachloads of pissheads turning up in ever increasing numbers. No gear and even the odd bit of aggro going about. And the heavy heavy police presence as the plod tried to clamp down harder than ever on the out of control drug scene.

So one night after an expensive meal, we arrived outside the Casino with our now regular girlfriends, wanting to know what it was all about. The large neon letters proclaiming Wigan Casino were still there and lit up, but there were hardly any crowds outside like there used to be. No mass of people queuing up in agony to get in the club. There was plod everywhere, checking people out to see if they were carrying. They gave us the once over before we went into the Beachcomber to see who we could find. There were no familiar faces in evidence inside, just loads of grief off the girlfriends for bringing them to such a dump of a club. Their education had been Blackpool clubland and quite different to the rough, ready and run down vibe of Wigan Casino. We just had time for a quick Coke and a bag of crisps, and then it was up to the main hall to see if we could spot a few friendly heads.

Once in the main hall, the buzz was as good as it had ever been and we made our way over to the Blackpool corner where we were certain we'd bump into a few of the crew for sure. It was packed out and the sounds were blasting out as loud as they'd ever done, but there was a change in the air. There was nobody we knew in the old corner. Not one familiar face as we searched in vain, so it was up to the balcony to look. More grief from my girlfriend and this time it was about the music. She was hating the experience, but at least she could tell people she'd been to Wigan Casino.

We dumped the bags down and looked around to see if there was anybody we knew lying around. There were a couple of guys we got talking to who seemed pleased to see us and wondered where the fuck all the Blackpool crew had gone. They just sort of stopped coming they told us. A few of them turned up for the odd one, but there were no regulars on the scene. They also told us it was useless to try and score gear as there was nothing about, and if we did sort some, it would be shit. Most people were worried about bringing it into the club for fear of getting busted by the plod. It seemed that all the rumours floating about in Blackpool were true, and the message hit home that the Casino had changed for the worse as we wandered around the balcony thinking we'd just got out in the nick of time.

We walked into Mister M's and were greeted by the usual intense heat and the smell of deodorant sprays, and managed to come across several faces we knew well who all too readily confirmed that the Casino was on the decline and that it would only be a matter of time before the club closed down forever. They spoke of much the same thing as the others had that night. Heavy plod presence. No gear and plenty of agg with the locals who'd had a bellyful of these weird soul freaks invading their town every Saturday night.

From where we stood, the Casino had lost all the ingredient's that kept us coming back each and every weekend. Doubtless, many people had returned as we had that evening only to find that the vibes had all but disappeared. The sounds and the DJs were still there, but precious little else was left of Wigan Casino. It didn't stop us from slipping back in time though, to remember what the Casino stood for and what made it the absolute number one club in the country for such a long time.

They were intense, occasionally desperate, totally hedonistic days that were impossible to recapture, no matter how hard you tried. No matter how much gear you took. That last all nighter was a numbing affair. Like a bad trip to the dentist. You know it's going to hurt but you keep telling yourself it won't. And then when you are sitting in the big chair, you realise it is going to hurt like fuck.

The hours dragged by. Something that wouldn't happen at an all nighter in the old days. Six hours would just fly by before you really had time to take it in, and you'd be heading for the exit before you knew it. Such was the intensity of enjoyment created by that unique Wigan Casino recipe. Your appetite was never satisfied, and you always wanted more. But over the years, the recipe had somehow managed to stay on the cooker too long, and the ingredients had boiled to nothing. All the taste had simply evaporated and there was nothing else left.

Just before the end, we collected our bags and walked past the old Blackpool corner that had been our home for the six years we were regulars at the all nighters. The sunlight was slowly beginning to filter through the dirty stained glass window as it had done hundreds of times before, signalling the end of another all nighter. The last three were playing out as regularly as the sun had raised its head. *Long After Tonight Is All Over* by Jimmy Radcliffe. *Time Will Pass You By* by Tobi Legend and *I'm On My Way* by Dean Parrish. The last sound of every all nighter.

We walked through the double doors, down the stairs and into the morning light for the last time. Never seeing or setting foot in the old building again, and finally bringing to a close, a deeply passionate, sometimes illogical, and often desperate, six year relationship with Wigan Casino.

An application to renew the club's licence was turned down by the powers that be, and in December 1981, Russ Winstanley stood at the decks for the final time. Wigan Casino closed down forever and in the process, brought to an end its involvement with a uniquely enigmatic underground music culture that contributed much to the English music industry.

This country, although small in size, has consistently given birth to both highly original music and youth cultures that have not only stood the test of time, but which have influenced teenagers the world over. You only have to look at the effects punk rock has had on music and fashion all over the globe, just one example of a youth culture born and bred in the UK and exported abroad. The teds, the rockers, the skins,

94

the mods, the punks, the ravers and the new age travellers have done much the same. Each with their own distinctive look, music, attitudes and ways of going about their business. And in amongst all these cultures you have to include the largely underground northern soul scene and the soulie, out on the dancefloor doing things his or her way. In baggy cords, leather soled shoes and tee shirts. Dancing away to his favourite sounds.

It was and still is a unique youth culture born out of the best traditions of British youth cultures. It had energy, enthusiasm, dedication, friendliness and notoriety, and although it will never be commercial and will always remain underground, it will never die. It just gets handed down from father and mother to offspring as if some valued antique family heirloom. The scene is still very much alive these days. Alive and kicking with the centre of the northern scene, ironically enough, based down in the depths of the 100 Club in Oxford Street in London. A club that manages to pack them in like they did at The Torch, Twisted Wheel, Catacombs, Va-Vas, Cleethorpes and Wigan Casino. The all nighters are back in the North as well, with the old Ritz ballroom about to enjoy a new lease of life spinning northern soul. Thanks to people who have given their everything to the northern scene, it will never die and will always be around in some form or another. Kev Roberts, ex-Wigan Casino man and record business owner summed it up absolutely perfectly when he wrote, "The North West of England, the undisputed leader of an underground phenomenon stretching back as far as 1968, and enjoying a new lease of life with the thirty somethings. I liken northern soul to marriage. You love it, live with it, leave it and then return to it."

He couldn't have put it any better and this applies to all who still work hard pushing it out to as many people as possible. People like Richard Searling, Ady Croasdale, Marc Bicknell, Pete Haigh, Roger Banks, Kev Roberts, Maurice Jones, Douggie The Disc and all the other fanatics who seem to get stronger as the years fly by. There's too many of them to name individually but they are out there every weekend, doing it and keeping the scene more than alive.

Wigan Casino, during the eight years it remained open, put northern soul on the map and although it wasn't the be all and end all of the northern scene, many would argue that it was the pinnacle. The ultimate experience. If you wanted all nighters that contained all the essential ingredients - atmosphere, top sounds and gear - then you'd catch a train, thumb a lift or jump a bus to the Casino because that's where you would find them. Get in the main hall and sample for yourself the magical buzz of a Wigan all nighter. And you'd agree as the last record played out, and you were covered in sweat and flying at a hundred miles an hour, that there was simply nothing like it. The Casino experience.

We were all totally gutted when they finally pulled the plug on the Casino, but it got crazy in the end and couldn't go on. From the first night it opened, the club was destined to be closed down, because the gear scene, very much a part of Casino life, and the very fuel it ran on, was always going to contribute to its downfall.

But it took them eight years to do it, and in that time, so many people joined the scene and became members of Wigan Casino. Shared so many unforgettable experiences there, and what came out of Wigan gave birth to another underground youth scene of more recent years.

When it was good at Wigan, it was fucking brilliant, especially during the club's heyday, which many regard as the years between 1973 and 1977. That's when the place really fired on all four cylinders and kept us all going back for more and more. But it wasn't always kind to you, the northern scene. It fucked you off at times and now and then it froze you to the bone. It demanded all your energy, at times just to get there on a Saturday night, and it offered you the chance to drop as much gear down your neck as you could possibly swallow. And as a result of this temptation, a few people paid the price for that over indulgence. But when you are mixed in with a bunch of gear dropping heads every Saturday night for the better part of six years, then there are bound to be a few casualties. No matter how slight they are though, it's still sad when somebody decides to do one.

Mixed in with all that nocturnal dancing, drug-taking hedonism that was Wigan Casino, there's bound to be a few regrets when people look back to those crazy days of northern soul. Cock ups that took people years to sort out, but most people managed it in the end. You can't have it all your own way all of the time. Overdose on enjoyment and not pay a price or have a few regrets. I can look back to those never ending mental nights as a Casino-goer, when the club became the only reason for drawing breath, when the all nighters were everything to me and more, and I find a couple of regrets. There will always be unanswered questions when people look back and think about what life might have been. One question keeps coming back to me and I can only guess at the answer. If I hadn't found the Casino, what would it have been like to fly fast jets for a living?

Keep On Keeping On

O n Saturday night, June 3rd, 1995, I made a long awaited return to the northern scene. I'd been to a number of soul nights and very enjoyable they were too. But an all nighter. They are different. Special. The difference between gold and silver.

So we were off to Blackburn for an all nighter. Ged, who was there from the beginning, Crazy Larry, a local DJ on the house scene and one time northern soul fanatic, Chris, a long standing friend who had northern soul as bad as we did, but handled it a lot more sensibly, and his girlfriend Josephine who came along to discover what it was all about after we'd bored her shitless for hours discussing the northern scene, and how it just kept on going and going after all these years. We were to look for a venue called Tony's Melody Ballroom, tucked away down some side street in the town centre.

I couldn't wait for it. All the old feelings were still there inside me. The buzz of driving to another town to dance the night away to music that had played such a part in my life. Steaming down the M6 with the cassette blasting out some old well familiar northern monsters. It felt like we'd never been away from the scene. Just that feeling of doing something different. Doing something nocturnal. It just couldn't be beat.

I didn't know what to expect of the scene these days. I had heard many stories about it. That it couldn't be compared to those mental nights in the Casino, but looking at it realistically, what could? The scene in those days peaked higher than we all thought possible, and the Casino was the centre of it all. Nothing could ever compare to that. It's impossible to look back to those days and judge what is going on today. That's a shit one and totally negative, and besides nothing stays the same. Not after twenty years, but the important thing is that the northern scene is still around, well and truly alive, with events going off all over the country. That's enough.

I was still full of expectation as I climbed the stairs of the Melody Ballroom at midnight, handed the girl behind the paydesk my seven

97

quid and went into the ballroom. And I was pleasantly surprised at what I discovered as that unique sounding music drew me into a well attended venue that just has to be seen to be believed. I don't know where the fuck the promoters keep managing to come up with such venues, but thank God that they do. These old faded quirky venues, that have seen better days before most of the northern crowd were even born, seem the perfect hosts of all nighters. The Melody is run down, but not too badly. The paint's faded and cracked, and it's rough and ready with a smell all of its own, but somehow, it's just right for an all nighter. And the tea served up in the back bar area is the business. Just the stuff you need when you begin to flag as the hours pile up on you.

That evening I came as an observer. Not as a dancer or gear freak, but simply an observer. To discover and soak up all the vibes the place and the people gave off. See how the scene had survived some fourteen years after the Casino had said goodbye to its last punter. And there was plenty to observe and soak up too.

The music was as good as ever. Admittedly a fair number of the sounds played were new to our ears, but still excellent to hear. And there were a fair few more familiar sounds too that kept the four hundred or so people happy, and more importantly, on the dancefloor. Which is what an all nighter is all about. And some of the dancers were just out of this world as they went through brilliant to watch routines on the crowded dancefloor. It took me back to that first time at Wigan when I stood on the balcony to watch a mass of humanity going through similar routines. All of them dancing with a passion to a music that is celebrating its thirtieth birthday since its introduction to the UK. Dancers who were much younger than the actual music, but that made no difference at all as they went through some classic northern footwork. Some of them topped up on gear and others not, flying up and down the dancefloor.

In one corner a young woman held court. In black trousers and sleeveless top, and with her long black hair tied into a ponytail that flowed down her back as she danced her arse off, combining ballet style moves with northern spins and footwork that was just brilliant to watch. Athletic and elegant, she interpreted the music with her own definitely original style of dancing, only stopping occasionally to towel off and take a swig of refreshment before returning to her corner of the ballroom to go through her routine again and again. Brilliant.

And just in front of where we were sat by the edge of the dancefloor were a couple of guys who were doing the business. And how. They looked pretty similar in looks and build so they could have been brothers. I don't know, but could those guys dance. One wore a sleeveless tee shirt and the other was topless, and both had sun tans and bodies that were born after hours in the gym getting fit. I tell you, if Michael Winner had walked in looking for a couple of northern soul dancers to audition for a film about the scene, then those two guys would have instantly caught his eye and been offered a part in it. They didn't come off the dancefloor the whole time we were at the all nighter. A couple of northern soul dervishes if ever there were two. They'd be gliding around the floor effortlessly to the beat of the music and then all of a sudden, go into spins, backdrops and painful looking splits, and then back into the footwork as if nothing had happened.

There were others too. Plenty of good dancers we spotted on that dancefloor in that dark ballroom, but it just happens that those three deserve a particular mention as they just stood out above the rest of the crowd.

Away from the dancefloor and in the equally crowded back bar area, it was a hive of activity with record dealers selling to eager punters who were thumbing through boxes of northern soul records. One of the dealers is possibly the scene's most eccentric character. Robin the record dealer who has been on the scene a long time. But how many of us want to change sex? Not many I bet, but there was Robin at the Blackburn all nighter, dressed as his alter ego, complete with wig, lipstick, black jacket and skirt and white blouse. Standing there behind his record stall as if he's been dressing as a woman all his life. And he probably has! Apparently he is saving up for the full sex change operation. Not exactly my cup of tea Robin, but if it makes you feel good, if it makes you happy, then go ahead and do it. The path you have chosen for yourself takes a lot of courage to walk down, so good luck to you.

Dave Rimmer was there too and it was great meeting him after all the letters that had passed between us with regard to the book, and for me it was great to meet one of the people who had actually taken the time to sit down and contribute to the book. Dave is behind a magazine called *A Soulful Kinda Music* and is well respected on the northern soul scene by all and sundry. His knowledge of northern soul is second to none, and if you feel you would like to get to know more about this music and the scene, then you could do no better than get your hands on a copy of his magazine.

And out in the crowded corridor, amid mouthfuls of that fantastic tea, I met a guy called Saus, who like Dave Rimmer has given his life to this unique underground movement. He is now forty years of age, but you wouldn't think so listening to him talk about the scene and the music he loves with a passion and a knowledge that will never be extinguished. He's a good DJ too and well liked by many people on the scene. After ten or fifteen minutes, he gets you into thinking that you have known him for years. A really cool, laid back, friendly guy, who is prepared to spend time with you and tell you just what you want to know, providing you are willing to listen to what he has to say, and that night I definitely was. Saus is dedicated to the scene. Today's scene more than yesterday's scene, and he was quite critical of looking back to Wigan Casino and seeing it as the be all and end all of the northern soul scene in this country. He's dead right too. The club was undoubtedly very important to the northern scene and its development, but without the scene, there would be no clubs and that's so important to keep in mind.

He talked of today's northern punters who are more knowledgeable than their predecessors. They want to know about the music, and one way or another, they find out about it. And they are far less intent on getting out of their skulls on gear than we were. Sure there is gear around if you want it and, no doubt, people will find it as enjoyable as we did because to some people, an all nighter isn't an all nighter without a wrap of gear. And apparently, the Blackburn all nighter is the gear all nighter, so if you are going to drop gear, then Blackburn is the one to do it at. Myself, I like the fact that gear isn't number one on the list of priorities on today's scene, and we certainly kept going without the need for it. The sounds, the people and the atmosphere were enough for us that night, and we left the eccentricity of the Melody Ballroom with more than a pleasant taste in our mouths.

For me, I was well pleased with what I'd seen and heard from all concerned, and more importantly, totally convinced that the northern scene will never die so long as it remains in the hands of people like Saus and Dave Rimmer who have dedicated their lives to it and have come to know every aspect and what makes it tick. And there are others, young and old, who will make sure that this enigmatic underground scene will remain a part of this island's culture. From St. Ives to Edinburgh, there is a flourishing rejuvenated northern scene that is out there just waiting to be discovered by the uninitiated. From back rooms in pubs to old ballrooms, the northern soul scene is kicking thanks to a whole host of people, some more well known than others, who turn out continually, weekend after weekend with their boxes of records to keep the punters happy.

The old guard are still active too, keeping an eye on its continual development. Dave Rimmer's still got the bug for the music after discovering northern way back in 1973. Want to know what it means to him and how he got into it? Well he can tell it for himself. "What a question. It's like the meaning of life! What is it that still drags me out of the house nearly every Saturday night to spend a couple of hours travelling, then eight hours in a dimly lit dancehall, then another couple of hours travelling back? The simple answer is, I still don't know! It started a long time ago though, back in 1973.

"In 1973 I was the typical pimply youth who was just learning about many things. It was a time for discoveries, sex, cigarettes, best bitter and the lure of the dancefloor in northern soul discos. I grew up just outside Warrington, a town which through The Carlton Club has a long history of playing black music. But I was still at school then so what attracted me to soul music? At most schools in the north west in those days, the choice was made for you. You either liked soul music or you didn't. If you didn't you liked long hair (on men) and smelled slightly of motorcycle oil. Well, I've never been particularly mechanically minded and anyway in those days, I preferred the smell of Brut so I became a soul fan. It wasn't an overnight conversion though. I used to buy all sorts of records. It's just that I gradually realised I was buying mostly soul records, probably influenced by the fact that the lunchtime school discos played a continuous diet of soul music. It was this and the fact that the discos were run by a mate's older brother so we got in free, that introduced me to the music. It was the records that I heard there that I was buying with my pocket money and the dinner money my mum gave me faithfully every day. I dieted and saved the money to send off a postal order on the Friday. I also heard tales of the Golden Torch ballroom in Stoke On Trent that some of the older lads were going to. All night as well! Eventually I plucked up enough courage to tell my parents I was staying at a mate's overnight, and I went to an all nighter at Va-Va's in Bolton. That settled it. I was hooked.

"This was the period when you could go out any night of the week and find a pub or even a youth disco or club within ten miles, that was holding a northern soul disco. They were still called discos then and it hadn't become a dirty word. The records were all new, exciting and because of the scene being so busy, a new sound could be broken within a month. You'd probably hear it twice a week. There were also the new friends you made. Friends who you still have today, almost twenty five years later.

"So that was the introduction to the music, but what does it mean to me? Well that period of my life holds so many memories, it has always been in retrospect, wonderful. Let's face it. You always remember the good times, and view things through rose tinted glasses. And we did have good times!

"As I mentioned earlier, the other discoveries were also important. Sex was, but you never considered going out with a girl who wasn't into northern. Best bitter, and hangovers. Parties where the neighbours called the police because you'd played *Mr Bang Bang Man* fourteen times in a row at full volume. There were cigarettes and other substances and throughout, the steady beat of soul music that provided a constant musical background.

"So many memories and all catered for in and around a tatty run down dance hall in Wigan which was the focus of the whole week. I'm sure other writers have said all there is to say about the Casino so I'll not dwell on the place, just the era. By 1978, I'd accepted a job in North Wales which involved me starting work at 6.00am on a Sunday morning, so that was the last of the scene for a while for me. However this was the period when I really developed into a soul music fan, rather than a northern soul fan. My own musical tastes matured and I concentrated my record buyer trips on albums rather than singles. It still was outside the mainstream music Joe Public knew though. That's something that the scene always had and will always retain. The feeling of being one of the elite. One of the in crowd. One of the few lucky enough to be let into a secret of what real music is. Snobbery? Of course but why the hell not! We all know that the only type of music that really matters is soul music. Don't we?

"I digress. I moved to the Midlands in 1981 with very few singles but quite a large album collection. Got married, had children, bought a house and got on with my career. The northern soul scene was dead, a part of my youth albeit a large part of it, that was now just happy memories. How wrong I was!

"Unknown to me, when the Casino closed, the scene just didn't die. It moved on to my home town of Warrington, Stafford, and London (unbelievably). It didn't die in the Midlands either, once a real hotbed for the scene. It just went back underground. I kept seeing adverts for northern soul nights in Wolverhampton so eventually (with my wife's permission) I went to one in about 1986. I remember walking in and thinking that I wouldn't know anyone, until Pedro from Wolverhampton came over and said, 'I know you. You're a Bolton Wanderers fan from Culcheth. What are you doing here?'

"It was just like old times. The music was the same (it was an oldies night) and I thoroughly enjoyed myself. I was hooked all over again.

"So here l am, twenty two years on and still doing nighters and soul nights, and in my own way, trying to put something back into the scene through the magazine I edit. *Soulful Kinda Music*. I realise that I still haven't answered the question though . . . what does northern soul mean to me? Here goes then. It's a feeling, a lifestyle, a love of the music, friends from all over the country, the joy at hearing a record you love, the greater high of managing to buy a copy of that record. The atmosphere at a nighter. The anticipation of next weekend's nighter. The DJs, the venues. It gets in your blood and it never goes away. Also for me these days, it's the thirst for knowledge to know more about the people who made those magical records twenty, even thirty years ago.

"I've again taken the rose coloured glasses view of course. I've ignored the bad aspects of the scene, but why dwell on the down side when we have such a strong, vibrant, knowledgeable and alive scene. As an entity, it cannot be controlled by one person, but it does have a persona of its own and the continuing development of that persona, the change in the venues, the records, the tempo, the continuous changing thread of people will ensure that the northern scene will survive, reduced in size maybe, but just as devoted and committed!"

Howard Earnshaw has similar beginnings in the northern scene, and tells it like it was, and is. "My first taste of soul and the soul scene was at the local discos of Huddersfield, with names like The Starlight, Lord Jims and The Hi-fi Discotheque. All names that will live in my memory. This is where I was introduced to the heady sounds of Stax, Atlantic and of course, Tamla Motown, progressing from Rufus Thomas and The Memphis Train to Junior Walker and the thumpin' *Pucker Up Buttercup!* The whole mod thing at the time excited me. The suits with ridiculously deep centre vents and large flap pockets. The Ben Sherman shirts and highly polished brogues. The one black driving glove. Oh yes - and then there were the girls with their immaculate hairstyles. Short fringes and extra long side pieces, and being in with the in crowd, looking down on anyone who didn't fit in. We were untouchable!

"It wasn't long after that the magic word 'import' hit my ears and we started travelling further afield to hear the music that we cared so much for, and then making my first trip to the Twisted Wheel, remembered as much for the music as for being rolled before I reached the club, and being relieved of my money. Then it was onto clubs that will be familiar to all those who have an ounce of soul in their bodies. The Torch, The Pendulum, Samanthas, Hinckley, Clifton Hall, Blackpool Mecca and of course, the one club that the whole world came to know about. Wigan Casino.

"I remember my first visit. Initial thoughts were this is the perfect all nighter venue. The balcony was overlooking the swirling bodies, the smell, the sounds in that first year. There was no competition from any other venue. It was just the place to go and in amongst all that, I was married, divorced, and married again. In the scene. Out of the scene (but never truly out) and of course well into the whole thing again!

"So here I am now. Older, yes, but still committed to that friendly esoteric soul music thing that hooked me in 1967 and continues to please and entertain me in 1995. And what doesn't surprise me in the least is that there are hundreds of others out there that are still experiencing that same buzz. Well that's what soul meant and still means to me . . . Keep on keeping on."

Garry White, one of the men who continue to keep Barrow well and truly on the northern soul map has memories galore. "My first introduction to soul music was back in 1969 at my local youth club. Somebody brought in a few records to play, the first being Al 'TNT' Braggs' *Earthquake* (consequently this was the first record I ever bought), followed by the O'Jays' *I Dig Your Act*. From then on I was hooked. By the time I was fifteen, I was attending our local rugby club's twice weekly soul sessions and the atmosphere was fantastic. In those days it was either soul music, scooters and yellow braided blazers etc, or Black Sabbath and leather. There was no contest.

"Blackpool Mecca was soon beckoning. At this time I was playing football in and around the Blackpool area on Saturdays, and after the game, I would go through to Preston, to the record shop in the bus terminal. There always seemed to be something I wanted in there. Then it was back to Blackpool for a couple of pints and to wait for my mates to come through from Barrow. The Mecca in those days was a whole new world. Ian Levine and Colin Curtis spinning the sounds. 'Who's This?' 'Tony Clarke', came the answer. 'It's bloody brilliant', and so it went on.

"Over the next year or so, I ventured further afield, to the Top Rank in Hanley, Va-Va's in Bolton, Samantha's in Sheffield and then the night that I will always remember. My first night at the Casino. The club had already been open a couple of months and I'd had lots of good reports about it. So at 9 o'clock I jumped on the train in Barrow. It was only when we reached Lancaster that the atmosphere hit home. People piled on in droves and then a dozen or so tape recorders clicked on. The tunes and the faces of those people were about to be etched on my mind forever. I remember arriving in Wigan just after eleven, and thinking, *What am I going to do for three hours?* Then in the background someone said "Chippy, and then the Beachcomber". *Beachcomber?* I thought, *Where's that?* So I went in with a few of my mates. The chips were good, but the Beachcomber was something else. Golden oldies, backdrops and records for sale.

At one thirty, we joined the queue, and the talk was all about what was played last week. And what would be played this week and then the doors opened at two o'clock. Call me stupid, but I wasn't quick enough for what happened next. I went one way and my holdall went twenty yards the other way. It took me several minutes to reclaim my bag, and then it was up the stairs. People were already dancing and others were piling holdalls into corners. *This is brilliant*, I thought. By eight in the morning, when Jimmy Radcliffe came on, I was knackered but then it was down to the baths for a swim and something to eat. The journey back to Barrow was another experience. Reliving the night on the many tape recorders.

"Over the next few years I visited the Casino many many times, although for various reasons, not as often as I wanted. Every trip had its own story. Like the night Tommy Hunt was on. My sister informed me that she had had her vanity case stolen with everything in it, including money and train ticket. Have you ever tried smuggling someone on and off a train and have your ticket checked as well? Believe me it's not easy, but we managed it. Needless to say this did not deter us. Just made us more vigilant. Now twenty years later, along with Bob Reilly, we still have a successful soul scene up here in Barrow. The records I had at home and thought were out of date are now back once again and filling the floor. Thanks to Richard Searling, who along with Pete Smith in Hastings, has given me invaluable assistance and advice over the last couple of years, I think we can go on a lot longer. Keep the faith."

Ian Palmer recalls his thoughts and feelings on a scene that he has put in thousands of miles attending over the years. "Where do you start when somebody asks you to put in writing your thoughts and feelings about this music scene? After all, the northern scene was a bit like the Sixties. If you can remember it, then you weren't really there! But through the blur I laughingly call my memory, there are certain moments that seem as clear to me now as the day they really happened. I was too young to go to clubs like The Twisted Wheel and The Torch, and so my first introduction to the real northern scene was in late 1974, when after what seemed like an eternity travelling the one hundred and sixty miles north, followed by hours of queuing in the freezing night air, I found myself for the first time walking out onto the balcony at Wigan Casino. As if on cue, the intro to LeRoy's *Tears* blasted out of the speakers and the whole place went wild. I had never seen a crowd react in such a way. People ran down stairs to grab the few remaining spaces on the dancefloor, or just jumped up and started dancing where they were. To this day, when I recall that night I still remember the heat and smell of the place. I was hooked.

"That was twenty one years ago and after dabbling in various forms of music both as a punter and musician, I find that something keeps calling me back, and here I am thirty five years old and visiting more all nighters than I ever did in those days. Probably because at the time, few lads could afford cars or train fares so the long journey north could only be made once or twice a month when cash permitted. Luckily for us, in this part of the country we had the regular Yate all nighters which were easier to get to and blessed with the craziest crowd of people in the country. I remember hitch-hiking to the Casino a few times with Dave Thorley who lived in the same small Gloucestershire town as I did at that time, and the man I blame for really getting me into all this. It used to take practically all weekend. Sometimes we wouldn't get back until the early hours of Monday morning. Dave of course went on to be a well known DJ, and ran Stafford all nighters during the Eighties. A venue which helped to keep the northern flame burning after the closure of the Casino. But I think that the nomadic nocturnal lifestyle that most dedicated soul fans lead is half the appeal. I'm sure we all have memories of great times spent travelling to and from obscure far away places to go to all nighters, some of which may well have been crap, but the journey made up for it. But this scene

106

shouldn't just be about memories. I know that I'm having just as good a time now as I was then, but I admit I don't miss the hitching home bit now that I can drive everywhere in the comfort of a warm car.

"It was while I was returning from an all nighter about eighteen months ago. The Ritz I think. Anyway I suggested to Dennis Lee, a good mate of mine since those earliest Casino days and Yate all nighters that what the scene needed was a magazine. One that focused on the brilliant scene, social wise, that surrounds the northern scene. The scene always had more than its fair share of characters, and I would certainly include Dennis in that list. And so, a few months later the first issue of *Manifesto* was born, and in one year, it has grown to be the best selling fanzine on the soul scene.

I think at first people were suspicious of us, probably thinking we were out to make money from the scene and wondering what two lads from down south thought they were doing producing a magazine about northern soul. But I like to think that over the last year they have seen the work that we have put into it to make it succeed, and have therefore responded with genuine support and friendship. And besides, it's a well known fact that if you want to make money out of a music scene, then you don't choose northern soul. It was through *Manifesto* that I came to learn of Pete's plans to publish this book and I can't wait to read it. Sure there has been plenty written and even film documentation of the northern scene, but it has to be said that to date, nothing has been done that improves northern soul's naff public image. However we're all twenty years older and wiser and many of us are in a position to help rectify that, and in doing so, help to attract new blood, or simply get back some of those, who like myself, had moved on to other things over the years and now need a little persuasion to draw them back. After all, no other music scene has lasted this long and judging by the number of venues dotted around the country, it shows no signs of dying out yet. So if you are reading this book simply out of curiosity about the northern soul phenomenon, then do yourself a favour and check out a soul night, or better, one of the big all nighters, and you will hear some of the most exhilarating and varied dance music ever recorded. And if you are one of those soul fans who have given it up for whatever reason, find your way back if you can. You might be surprised at how many of your old mates are still about."

Ady Croasdell, one of the main men on the scene still and the driving force behind Kent Records writes of his recollections of some of the early stamping grounds he visited when discovering northern soul.

"Kelmarsh, Northants. The first. Only four miles from my home town. It started off as a poorly attended soul disco playing Stax, Motown and Geno, etc etc and at midnight it turned into the coolest club ever. A hundred skinheads (we were still mods and I had shoulder length hair) descended on the place with copies of the Esquires, Tony Clarke, the Fascinations and many more, opening my eyes to a whole new world.

"Bletsoe, Bedfordshire. The basics. Okay. So Kelmarsh was only a disused railway station but this place was a genuine barn. The decks were powered by a generator brought in for the night and the floor was rough concrete which left your DMs covered in dust after a couple of plays of *I Don't Want To Discuss It*. We liked them very fast then.

"The Lantern, Market Harborough. Nighters come to my home town. I exerted my first musical influence, telling the local DJ to ditch *Knock On Wood* and play *The Right Track*. Martin Ellis and the Manchester smoothies came down with *A Quitter Never Wins* and *Real Humdinger*. One of my mates paid four pounds for *Hooked By Love*. Totally incomprehensible to me.

"The Torch. Going up with the second known copy of *Times A Wastin'* with Dave Burton. Got us the VIP treatment. My biggest all nighter up to that date but I still preferred the local smaller dos, even though we didn't have *Inky Winky Wang Dang Do*.

"Saints And Sinners, Birmingham. The ultimate underground. In the middle of Birmingham city centre. You had to walk through an all night cafe filled with people only slightly less dubious than ourselves. Through a door and along several corridors and into the bowels of the earth. The final door would open and you'd see a small, red lit room with minimal dancefloor and fifty to a hundred people of your own all night crowd.

"The Birds Nest, West Hampstead. Only an evening do with Dave Burton, Dave Rivers and Mick Smith DJing some of the best and biggest sounds of the time. *The Catwalk. I Got Something Good. Just Like The Weather*. Very large green and clears. Carlsberg Special Brews and Mandies. From the only five strong skinhead gang at London University at the time. Keen but messy.

"The Pier, Cleethorpes. We arrive to hear the dancefloor bouncing up and down in a very unique style. It had to be *The Champion* and it was. Why was I so popular after my first US trip? *Love Factory* for three pounds. Shane Martin for four."

"Yate, Bristol. In deep snow. Surely no one would have made it tonight. We were certifiable for even trying. The car park looked dead, but inside five hundred people were dancing like maniacs to Clarkie, playing a few sounds I'd passed onto him. Frankie And Johnny. Kiki Dee etc etc.

"Wigan. The big 'un. I went on one of the first nights and enjoyed it, but it was a bit too big and sparse. A year later it was too big and crammed. The crush at the door, the volume of people, the heat, the records, all made it slightly surreal. We were the boys in the record room, probably for the first time. I can't remember any dealers (in vinyl!) at the Torch. The DJs seemed to have a few ego problems and they sat on the stage with wives and girlfriends and favoured friends like a gathering of minor royalty. It was a bit beneath them to visit the record room and they generally sent their minions to find their sounds for them. It was a great experience, but I lost my respect for the place when Mick and I found the dreaded Tony Blackburn LP down Portobello Road. Cut the Kenny Gamble acetate *I'll Do Anything*, and not only did Minsh play it, but the divs danced to it. No thanks!

"A boozer in Hammersmith. I can't even remember the name of the pub. Just a small back room playing all the real sounds I'd missed the first time around because of my preoccupation with speed (of the beat). Bobby Bland, Chuck Maine. Impressions. Nina Simone. Brilliant friends and plenty of beer. Alcosoul!

"The Starlight. West Hampstead. Randy and my second venue where we consolidated the crowd and turned a generation of mods on, and still had fun. Probably typified by the cover of *For Dancers Only*. The black guy was the taxi driver who had come to pick up the bouncer who had just let off a fire extinguisher in the toilet. We got closed down when the place just became too ridiculous for the management to handle. Kenny Carlton, Johnny Nash and Carolyn Crawford.

"Stafford, more musical learning. Where did all these new records come from? I thought I knew about northern soul but who changed the playlist? A whole new set of friends, many of whom last to this day. This is the hardcore of the scene who keep on going regardless. Tommy Navaro, Eddie Day and Peanut Quacking Duck.

"The 100 Club, London. DJ fights. Girlfriend and sister fights. Rock stars in the cloakroom. People travelling from Yorkshire and Lancashire to hear northern soul records being played exclusively in the Smoke. All guest all nighters letting the punters play the records for the first time. First female DJ since Guy Stevens' Scene Club in the Sixties. Ridiculous amount of anniversaries. Anniversary singles usually late! Becoming boring. Having to be responsible to keep it going. I couldn't be one of the lads anymore learning to DJ. Latin soul. Big ballads. Unissued master tapes. The regulars! Real people. Thanks."

You will also find Dave Evison at all nighters behind the decks, spinning the sounds that have kept him firmly on the scene for nearly thirty years. His DJing career beginning unexpectedly as a young squaddie while serving over in Northern Ireland between 1968 and '72. The Sergeant Major asked him to step in for the civvie DJ who hadn't turned up for the do in the mess. Strange beginnings but he began his northern career in Stafford at The Top Of The World before going on to Wigan Casino where he established himself as Mr Oldies. A label that has stuck with him to this day, and one he regards with fond but mixed feelings as he looks back on the northern scene.

"Back in the early Casino days, things were different. The scene was growing rapidly and it had gone like a roller coaster through The Torch, and although it was The Wheel that really kicked it off, by the time it had got to the Casino, it had become a national phenomenon. From the one or two cars that made the long distance journey to the Wheel to fleets of coaches from all over the country turning up at the Casino. The music policy hadn't changed up until then, but the Casino oldies scene changed all that and I must say that I can probably be blamed for being the straw that broke the camel's back because the oldies scene took away the whole notion of what the scene was about, and as it grew in popularity, the audience began to divide. And there is something sadly missing from the northern scene these days, and it probably started at the Casino, and that's respect.

"When I used to go to the Torch and the Wheel, it used to feel a privilege to be there. It was a bit like being in the army. You did what you were told. You listened to what those guys were playing and looked up to them. Not to say Martin Ellis because it was Martin Ellis, but because he played great music and you never knew what he was going to play. And so, if after twenty years of DJing, anyone would like to pay me a compliment, it would be to come up to me after my spot and say, 'That was great Dave. I haven't heard that for years.'

"Don't get me wrong. I would have been happy to stand behind a cardboard cut out and have been mystery DJ at Wigan. It wasn't an ego trip. I genuinely wanted to educate those youngsters on the scene and give them the opportunity that had been mine ten years before. Listening to people whose musical tastes I respected and to whom, because of my respect for their knowledge, I listened. I know this must sound corny, but I feel that it is important. I have always wanted to be thought of as one of the lads. There is no room for superstars. There are names I could mention that tried the great 'I am' act, but soon realised that it doesn't work. The people who gained respect were, I like to think, people like myself who danced until it was time for their spot, did it and got back out on the floor. Admittedly it was hard to keep your feet on the ground when Wigan Casino was at its peak. It was huge. Constantly on TV and in the press, and it was very easy to get carried away with your ego."

Kev Roberts too is very active on the scene, both behind the decks and as the main man behind Goldmine Records, an outfit responsible for bringing out many northern soul compilation albums over recent years. Another of the original Casino jocks and still around doing his stuff after nearly thirty years on the scene. Kev was there only three weeks after Wigan Casino had started its rise to number one soul club, and his story is one of good times and potential fortunes lost. "I grew up in Mansfield and in my early teens, started going to youth clubs and discos. Hard core working class towns like Mansfield were very mod, skinhead and Motown oriented, and the first time I ever came across northern soul was at a place called The Folk House in 1968. There were a couple of real heroes there called Dave Presolloc and Paul Harrison, and they played things like *Our Love Is Getting Stronger* by Jason Knight and Jackie Edwards' *I Feel So Bad*, which were impossible to get. In 1970, when I was still at school, I got tipped off that there was a stall selling records in Mansfield market run by Brian Selby and John Bratton, who went on to create Selectadisc. Every Saturday afternoon their store would be full of soul boys from far and near who'd come to snap up the latest releases.

"In late '72, I got my first job as a DJ at a club in Nottingham called The Brit, with a small box of records which I had been collecting since leaving school. I couldn't even cue a record properly, but I'd been buying about two imports a week since leaving school and had built up this little collection, so I started to play The Brit and the crowd remained. It was about the time that Alan Day, who used to be DJ at Up The Junction, became a big name DJ and just before leaving Selectadisc, he took me to the Torch for the first time - December, 1972 and my first real introduction to the scene. The Torch was packed that night and my head was spinning. I didn't know half the records they played even though I thought I knew quite a bit. Then suddenly . . . WOW. The Younghearts' *A Little Togetherness*. *Sliced Tomatoes*. JJ

Barnes and *Please Let Me In*. I'd never heard any of them before and I thought it was wonderful. The next week I got the train, which was a hell of a journey. We were there waiting at the door at eight o'clock and from then on, I was hooked.

"Then one week after the Blackpool Mecca, the lads said 'We're off to Wigan again, Kev. Are you with us or not?' To which I replied, 'Oh, alright then'. So off I went to Wigan with my box of records, which I took to show off. It was September, 1973, and as I walked through the doors I thought, *Crikey, this is a big place*. It looked like there were about six hundred in that night and the place held two thousand five hundred. They were playing an awful lot of pressings. Stuff out on Jay Boy, etc etc and I thought this is crap. The Mecca's got the best rarities, which to be fair, it did at that time.

"I had not met Russ Winstanley before and I remember a bunch of lads from Nottingham giving him a really hard time. 'Have you got Patti Austin?'. 'Have you got *I'm Gonna Change* by The Four Seasons?' 'Have you got this that or the other?', and of course Russ was saying no. Somebody said, 'Well, why don't you put somebody on who has.' 'Like who?' was the reply. It was then I got shoved to the front and Russ said, 'Who are you?' 'Kev Roberts', I said, 'I'm from Nottingham.' Anyway he put me on and thanks to the helpful enthusiasm of my crowd from the East Midlands, I went down well. I must have made the right impression because Russ said, 'Do you want to work here every week?' and I said, 'Yeaahh!'.

"So to 1974, and of course the buzz word was northern soul. I was only seventeen years old and we were breaking new ground with a sound of our own. Songs like Lou Ragland's *I Travel Alone* and some more commercial stuff like *The Joker* and *Strings A Go Go*. Then the commercial angle crept in and music industry people started to appear. *Blues And Soul* were up there practically every week. Television cameras began to appear for the first time and Pye Records in particular began to latch on to what was happening, and they set up a division to start releasing things that would appeal to this new audience.

"Unlike the Torch and Wheel, which only ever got bad publicity for their drug culture, the Casino was getting good positive publicity and people were latching onto it. At its peak the Casino was pulling regular attendances of two thousand five hundred people and northern soul was a household name."

And what of Kev's lost fortunes? "After the Casino I decided to go to New York to see what I could find. Whilst there, I met Lloyd

Michels who had this demo disc of a track called *The Flasher* which I brought back to England hoping to get a record deal with. I approached 20th Century Records who had released *Reaching For The Beat*. They didn't want to know and so I went off to a reggae label called Creole in London who also didn't like it, but they put me in touch with Denis Berger who was the label manager for Route, who picked up on it and made it a big hit. It was even used as the theme tune on Radio One's *Newsbeat*, but I didn't make any money out of it because I was young and naive. It even featured on *Top Of The Pops*, and I was invited down to London to watch the recording, but I couldn't afford the train fare and was too busy talking northern. I just wanted to find records."

One fortune gone. And one to go. "During the late Seventies, I met up with a record buying customer of mine called Les McCutcheon from Weybridge in Surrey, who was a businessman. A little older than me and he knew what was what. He became my partner importing records and making things for Casino Classics like *I'm Gonna Share It With You*, and things like *Green Onions*. By Mod 1979, when *Quadrophenia* came out, we were dabbling in all sorts of music. There was an outfit who were making records for us called The Nicky North Band, who were friends of Les's down in Weybridge. They had a stab at a jazz funk record called *Steppin'* of which we pressed up a thousand copies on white labels and sold them to a store called The Record Shack, who then re-ordered it, by which time we needed a label so . . . Record Shack . . . Shakatak, and they went on to be signed by Polydor. I remember Les saying to me as clear as day. 'Are you in or out?' as we had only got a five hundred quid advance between the lot of us. I thought there was more money in trying to find another *Better Use Your Head* by Little Anthony And The Imperials than there was in this jazz funk game, so shortsightedly I let it go and Kev Roberts lost another fortune."

Very few scenes have that seemingly eternal hold on its followers, and there is still something magical in northern soul. Just listening to a particular track with the volume turned full on and the guy in the upstairs flat banging on your ceiling with his shoe in an attempt to turn it down. *Not a cat in hells chance mate, but don't worry. Only another couple of hours to go and I will be through.*

When Terry from Barrow says, and I quote, "It's a great stress reliever", I couldn't agree more because at times it can be just that. It can lift you to another place far away from the bank manager, the tax man and the accountant. It could then, and it still does now, despite it being thirty years old and somewhat out of place in a world that is now dominated by digital audio this and compact disc that. It can still hold its own to this day, and has done for me ever since Pete Haigh put *If You Ask Me* on his turntable all those years ago.

Don't ask me why because I can't give you an answer. It remains as much a mystery to me now as it did then. All I can say is that it was the first music I heard that had everything. A magic, a feel, an atmosphere, a rawness and a fuck off driving beat that buried everything. It felt right to my ears. Just right. Some things in life have that all encapsulating feel that in turn makes you feel the business, and very few things since have left me with a taste in my mouth like northern soul does.

You have got to be tuned into it or else it will do nothing for you at all. It will sound shit, as I have been told on numerous occasions by various people. Pinky and Perky music and all that bollocks. They would listen with the intention of giving it a good go. Try and get something out of it, but would soon give up the cause and leave the room. Some of them thinking that I'd lost my mind to that driving beat that was blasting out from my speakers and doing their heads in.

But that's northern for you. You either love it or hate it and that is that as far as I'm concerned. To those who love it, it is a lifelong companion and mood enhancer to cheer you up during those days when you couldn't feel any lower. And for an easy life, find yourself a partner who is into it as much as you are and the arguments just go away. If you are opposites, then it's a guaranteed kick off as soon as you turn up the system and go into one for a couple of hours. If you let it, it can fuck up your relationships in no time at all.

Holidays too, and in a big way. A mate of mine went to the States a few years ago when the northern scene was massive. Crazy Larry from Blackpool. A disc jockey on the house scene of more recent years but he still retains a love of northern soul, even if he is too knackered to give us a few spins and a backdrop these days. So he saved up all his pennies for the trip of a lifetime to the States, and on getting there, what does he do? Spend most of the holiday bumming around record shops in search of northern sounds, without too much success, but at least he tried, and more importantly, enjoyed trying. At least I think he did!

Jobs! They also went out of the window when the choice came between sticking with the all nighters or doing the sensible thing and walking away while you were ahead. My old mate Ged, who was there from the beginning, made his choice as far as that was concerned. He'd left school and was doing very nicely thankyou very much, employed as a trainee ophthalmic technician. Good long term prospects and a place paid at college by the boss too. Then he gets into northern soul and then Wigan Casino and the all nighters, and then a bit of this and a bit of that, and suddenly he's under pressure. Taking time off work and sleeping in on Mondays to catch up on the zzz's lost at the weekend. Then the job starts to take second place until one night the boss turns up at his house in a yellow convertible E-type. Just goes to show the money you can make in the spectacles game.

This guy was okay too. A real nice personality and full of concern for Ged, partly because he was under the manufactured assumption that my old mate was ill. The whole situation continued for a few weeks until the guy in the E-type turned up again and told Ged he wasn't able to keep his job open for him any longer unless he returned to work.

Ged was pretty crazy in those days, and cared little for anything that didn't have a driving beat to it and took place between the hours of two and eight in the morning. Anything else didn't seem to matter so he just told his boss to fuck off. And his boss did just that. Fucks off, and along with him, takes Ged's chances of a really good job.

He still had his northern soul and Wigan Casino, and as he says now when he looks back to that time, he wouldn't have missed it for the world. The Wigan Casino experience. It cost him a few years, as it did many of us, but he is well sorted now, and enjoying life I suspect, more than he ever imagined he would.

Like I say, I still find it impossible to describe the feelings northern soul evokes in me, and why it did play such a massive part in my life. But there have been a number of experiences over the years that have evoked similar feelings. The feeling of just right. Personal experiences that have brought a smile to my face and the same taste to my mouth that northern soul always managed to do. Like the time George Best cut through the Chelsea team on a windy, rain-filled muddy pitch. With nothing more than a swivel of his hips, he sent Bonetti, the Chelsea goalkeeper, sprawling on his arse, leaving George with an open net and a frantic crowd as the ball just meandered into the Chelsea goal.

Or watching the great Ille Nastase playing a set of tennis at Wimbledon while holding an umbrella in one hand and his racket, fully operational, in the other hand, as the rain came down. Just right. Or walking into Nat Dunsby's in Blackpool. An old well respected tailor who operates out of what is effectively a first floor bombsite. In you walk with your roll of finest wool worsted under your arm, and six weeks later he appears with a handmade suit that fits you like the proverbial glove. He hands it to you. You try it on and bingo. It fits you just right. Or if you are really fortunate (and I was), the first time you sit down in a Sixties Mark II Jaguar. Positioned behind that woodrimmed steering wheel. Surrounded by the finest leather, wilton and burr walnut. And a dashboard that wouldn't look out of place in Concorde. You just sit there and soak up the whole ambience of a thoroughbred piece of engineering. The whole feeling is just right. If you are wearing a Nat Dunsby at the time, then even better. And if Gina Bellman just happens to be in the front seat with you, then what more could you ask for, apart from a selection of the latest Kent CD compilations to help dissolve the miles as you head to Brighton and the Albion Hotel for the weekend of your life. Now wouldn't that be just right?

WIGAN
CASINO

**The Casino Soul Club,
Empress Hall, Wigan
Sept. 1973 to Dec. 1981**

The Memory Lives On

WIGAN CASINO SOUL CLUB IS CLOSING DOWN

WE NEVER REALLY HOPED TO HAVE TO ANNOUNCE THIS BUT DUE
TO NOT BEING ABLE TO NEGOTIATE A LONG ENOUGH LEASE AND
THE EFFECTS OF THE RECESSION, UNFORTUNATLEY IT IS
INEVITABLE.
MANY, MANY THANKS FOR YOUR MARVELLOUS AND SUCH LOYAL
SUPPORT IT REALLY IS A TEARFULL END FOR A WONDERFUL EIGHT
YEAR ERA SPREADING THE FAITH OF NORTHERN SOUL - WE'LL
NEVER FORGET YOU - WE HOPE YOU'LL NEVER FORGET US.

Russ Winstanley.

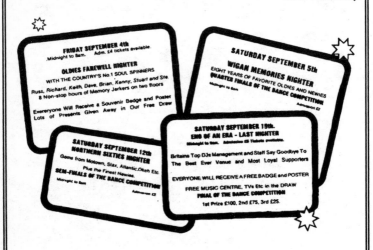

To Wigan Casino, Station Rd., Wigan, Lancs.
Friday Sept. 4th. LAST OLDIES NIGHTER
Please rush me...............TICKET(S) at £4.00 Each.
I enclose S.A.E. and P.O. for £..........

SATURDAY 19th. LAST NIGHTER
Please rush me...............TICKET(S) at £5.00 Each.
I enclose S.A.E. and P.O. for £..........

NAME.. TEL. No........................

ADDRESS..

....

....

....

118

WIGAN CASINO NEWS

SEPTEMBER 19th, 1981

Welcome to the Last Saturday Nighter

Due to the fantastic demand for tickets, and the fact that so many members have been unable to attend, we have managed to secure the Casino for just one more Oldies All-Nighter on

FRIDAY, OCTOBER 2nd, 12 Midnight to 8.00a.m.

We will be recording a Souvenir Album of the night featuring

TOMMY HUNT

DUE OUT AT CHRISTMAS
THIS WILL BE NORTHERN SOULS MOST HISTORICAL NIGHT

We also hope to announce details of our new venue
Britain's best D.J. Line Up (exclusive to the Casino) will be,
RUSS WINSTANLEY, KEITH MINSHULL, BRIAN RAE, DAVE EVISON AND GARY RUSHBROOKE
In Mr. Ms: KENNY SPENCE, STUART BRACKENBRIDGE and STE WHITTLE

TICKETS ARE ON SALE TONIGHT
at Reception after 3.30a.m.
Don't Miss Out - Tickets are £3.00

50 stone cold certified northern soul classics featuring artist, title, original US/UK label and year of release (or thereabouts) compiled by Pete Haigh, DJ, *Blues And Soul*, *Face* magazine contributor and BBC Radio Lancashire contributor. Some are 1960s classics and others are more recent discoveries. Some are even funky or jazzy, but all display that feel of a heady northern soul session. Many more could have been added to the list, but HEY!, Pete picked these off the top of my head.

1. Rufus Lumley . . . *I'm Standing* (Holton), 1966.
2. Tony Clarke . . . *The Entertainer* (Chess), 1965.
3. Fontella Bass . . . *Rescue Me* (Chess), 1965.
4. Dean Parrish . . . *I'm On My Way* (Laurie),1966.
5. Ike and Tina Turner . . . *Dust My Broom* (Tangerine),1965.
6. Morris Chestnut . . . *Too Darn Soulful* (Amy), 1967.
7. Earl Van Dyke . . . *6 by 6* (Motown Labels), 1966.
8. The Elgins . . *Heaven Must Have Sent You* (Motown Labels), 1965.
9. Frank Wilson . . . *Do I Love You* (Motown Labels), 1968.
10. Salvadors . . . *Stick By Me Baby* (Wise World), 1966.
11. Tomangoes . . . *I Really Love You* (Washpan), 1967.
12. Jackie Lee . . . *Darkest Days* (ABC), 1967.
13. R Dean Taylor . . .*Ghost In My House* (Motown Labels), 1967.
14. Gil Scott Heron . . . *The Bottle* (Strata East), 1974.
15. Gentlemen And Their Lady . . . *Like Her* (Roulette), 1974.
16. Ruby Andrews . . . *Just Loving You* (Zodiac), 1968.
17. Eddie Parker . . . *I Love You Baby* (Ashford), 1967.
18. Lew Kirton . . . *Heaven In The Afternoon* (TK Labels), 1977.
19. Brenda Holloway . . . *Reconsider* (Motown Labels), 1966.
20. Marvin Gaye . . . *Lonely Lover* (Motown Labels), 1966.
21. Willie Mitchell . . . *The Champion* (HI), 1964.
22. Bobby Paris . . . *Nite Owl* (Camco), 1964.
23. Ann Sexton . . *You've Been Gone Too Long* (Seventy Seven), 1971.
24. Yvonne Baker . . . *You Didn't Say A Word* (Cameo Parkway), 1965.
25. Gene McDaniels . . .*Walk With A Winner* (Imperial), 1965.
26. Young Holt Unlimited . . . *California Montage* (Brunswick), 1968.
27. Younghearts . . . *A Little Togetherness* (Canterbury), 1967.
28. Exciters . . . *Blowin Up My Mind* (RCA), 1969.
29. Sam Dees . . . *Lonely For You Baby* (SS INT), 1968.
30. Linda Jones . . . *I Just Can't Live My Life* (Loma Warner), 1968.
31. Barbara McNair . . *You're Gonna Love My Baby* (Motown), 1966.

32. Jimmy Radcliffe . . *Long After Tonight Is All Over* (Musicor), 1965.

33. Lou Johnson . . . *Unsatisfied* (Bigtop), 1965.

34. Williams/Watson . . . *Too Late*, 1976.

35. Montclairs . . . *Hung Up On Your Love* (Paula), 1972.

36. Platters . . . *Washed Ashore* (Musicor), 1967.

37. Jack Montgomery . . . *Dearly Beloved* (Sceptre), 1966.

38. Invitations . . . *Skiing In The Snow* (Dynatone), 1967.

39. Stanley Mitchell . . . *Get It Baby* (Dynamo), 1967.

40. JJ Barnes . . . *Sweet Sherry* (Groovesville), 1966.

41. Earl Wright . . . *Thumb A Ride* (Capitol), 1966.

42. Frank Beverley . . . *Is That What You Wanted* (Gamble), 1968.

43. O'Jays . . . *I Love Music* (Philadelphia Int), 1975.

44. Phillip Mitchell . . . *I'm So Happy* (Atlantic), 1978.

45. Jackie Wilson . . . *I Get The Sweetest Feeling* (Brunswick), 1969.

46. Major Lance . . . *You Don't Want Me No More* (Okeh), 1967.

47. Fascinations . . . *Girls Are Out To Get You* (Mayfield), 1966.

48. Ray Pollard . . . *The Drifter* (United Artists), 1966.

49. Joy Lovejoy . . . *In Orbit* (Chess), 1965.

50. Astors . . . *Candy* (Stax), 1965.

If you want to know more about today's northern scene then get your hands on one of the magazines available - Mark Bicknell's *Soul Underground* or Dave Rimmer's *Soulful Kinda Music*. Howard Earnshaw's *Soul Up North* or Ian Palmer's *Manifesto* and they will tell you all you want to know, what nights are on and where.

Then go and check out a night for yourself to see if you will get anything out of it or not. You can try Richard Searling's soul nights held at the King George Hall in Blackburn if you aren't up to an all nighter. Well popular these nights are proving to be, so get there early and you will enjoy a good session of floorshakers. Guaranteed. Or if you find yourself up in Barrow with nothing to do, drop in at Geronimos and be entertained by Garry White and Bob Reilly, the men behind the decks who have put their lives and a considerable portion of their cash into the northern scene and keeping it alive. They are all over the place so the choice is yours. Stockport, Hyde, Burnley, Nottingham, Crewe, Cambridge, Wigan, Rochdale, Norwich.

And if bigger venues are your thing then you can sample the flavour of the Ritz Ballroom in Manchester at an all night session or Keele. Two of the bigger all nighters on the scene that feature a range of guesting DJs who will keep you entertained for the evening. Dave Evison, Kev Roberts, Keith Minshull, Brian Rae, Ste Whittle and many others will be there with their assortments of floorpackers. And if you feel you have the energy, then you could do no better than sample one of Ady Croasdell's mammoth soul all weekenders up in Cleethorpes. An event that features two all nighters, two all dayers and a couple of evening seesions thrown in for good measure. Ady books good live artists too, many of them legends on the northern soul scene. For example this year's event featured none other than Tommy Hunt and Doris Troy. Tommy Hunt appeared at the Casino many times and even cut a brilliant live album in the club that conjures up so much of the Casino's special atmosphere when you sit and listen to it. And Doris is a legendary northern soul diva. And if just sitting and listening is your game, then there is plenty to choose from in the way of compact disc compilations these days. Send off for Ady Croasdell's Kent Records catalogue that features sounds that will appeal to everyone's taste in soul music. And Kev Roberts down at Goldmine Records who keeps coming up with excellent goods. So one way or another if it is your intention to find out more about the music and the scene, then it's all out there for you to discover.

Dave Evison summed it up perfectly in an interview with Richard Searling a few years ago. He said, "I firmly believe that in fifty years time, northern soul will be around in some form or another".

I couldn't agree more, Dave.

It's suicidal to print lists of contact addresses in the back of a book. Before the ink is dry on this page, someone will have moved. If you are interested in finding out more about today's northern soul scene, we will happily send a contact sheet to anyone who writes in with a stamped SAE (UK only) or an International Reply Coupon (IRC), available from any post office. Our address is S.T. Publishing, P.O. Box 12, Dunoon, Argyll. PA23 7BQ. Scotland.

If you enjoyed this book, there's a good chance you'll like our other titles . . .

Since 1991, S.T. Publishing has specialised in documenting street music and street youth cults. If you would like a copy of our latest catalogue, please write to the address below and ask for one. We send books to customers all over the world, and do our best to fill orders as soon as they arrive. A selection of our current titles are on the following pages.

We also welcome your comments on the book you have just read. Equally, if you are planning to write a book that may be of interest to us, please let us know.

S.T. Publishing
P.O. Box 12, Lockerbie, Dumfriesshire. DG11 3BW.   Scotland.

JOE HAWKINS IS BACK!

Available again at long last, the classic Richard Allen novels that charted the changing faces of British youth cults during the 1970s. Each volume contains three complete novels and there will be six volumes in the series. All are available from selected outlets or can be ordered direct from the publisher. For our latest mail order catalogue please write to S.T. Publishing, P.O. Box 12, Lockerbie, Dumfriesshire. DG11 3BW. Scotland.

THE COMPLETE RICHARD ALLEN VOLUME ONE
Skinhead   Suedehead   Skinhead Escapes

Three great novels in one book by the king of youth cult fiction, Richard Allen. SKINHEAD portrays with horrifying violence all the terror and brutality that has become the trademark of these teenage malcontents. SUEDEHEAD sees Joe grow his hair and swap his boots and braces for a velvet-collared Abercrombie coat. His aggro days are over - his city slicker days are just beginning. Joe's exploits of violence and anti-social behaviour were cut short by a prison sentence. But in SKINHEAD ESCAPES Joe Hawkins is on the loose again. With a vengeance to fulfil!

THE COMPLETE RICHARD ALLEN VOLUME TWO
Skinhead Girls   Sorts   Knuckle Girls

Three great novels in one book by Richard Allen. SKINHEAD GIRL gives a girl's eye-view of living for kicks. Joan Marshall was a skinhead at fifteen with all the savagery and excitement that went with it. SORTS are the Smoothies' girls. On the run from home, her skinhead lover and her memories, Terry Hurdy finds herself in a world of sex, drugs and - murder. And finally, meet Glasgow's Ina Murray in KNUCKLE GIRLS. Her violent upbringing taught her to fight for her rights - with a bicycle chain and copper wire surrounded by a circle of cheering supporters.

THE COMPLETE RICHARD ALLEN VOL. THREE
Trouble For Skinhead   Skinhead Farewell
Top-Gear Skin

Birds and aggro are never far from the mind of Joe Hawkins - even when he's sent to Dartmoor prison for killing a cop. But inside he's got other things on his mind - like the arrival of his old enemy, Charlie McVey. It all adds up to TROUBLE FOR SKINHEAD. In SKINHEAD FAREWELL, Joe finds himself blazing his way across Australia to nail down Charlie McVey once and for all! In TOP-GEAR SKIN, meet Roy Baird, the leader of a skinhead gang who needs more excitement than pulling birds and putting the boot in has to offer. For him, it's stockcar racing. And he'll do anything to come first.

THE COMPLETE RICHARD ALLEN VOLUME FOUR
Boot Boys   Smoothies   Terrace Terrors

First there were skinheads. Then came suedeheads. Now there are BOOT BOYS, ready to do battle on the terraces every Saturday afternoon. SMOOTHIES are the new villains of the peace, born out of the skinhead-suedehead cult. The aggro is always present - until they go too far! Then comes TERRACE TERRORS. Who better to tame the hooligans than Steve Penn and his crew of skins, suedes and boot boys from another era.

THE COMPLETE RICHARD ALLEN VOLUME FIVE
Mod Rule   Punk Rock   Dragon Skins

London Mods in Hastings riot! The war starts now. A biker splayed brokenly on the road, his machine wheel-spinning against the kerb. Other bikers roared their engines and bore down on Joe's crowd. It boiled down to a battle between nutty bikers and gutsy mods in MOD RULE. In PUNK ROCK, the punks are on the march and the teds are out to nobble them. Reporter Raymond Kerr meets the punks on their own ground to get his story. And when ex-skinhead Boots Welling joins a Kung Fu club, he finds his trainer is hoping to involve him in a series of crimes. But with the help of Steve Penn and the DRAGON SKINS he hopes to put a stop to it all.

THE COMPLETE RICHARD ALLEN VOLUME SIX will be available from April, 1997.

SPIRIT OF '69 - A Skinhead Bible
By George Marshall

For the first time, the history of the skinhead cult from the late
Sixties to the present day. Tradition, style, music, aggro. It's all
here as the skinheads tell their own story. Chapters include the
original skinheads, skinhead reggae, street punk, 2 Tone, Oi! and
fashion. Welcome to the land of the bovver brigade! SECOND
EDITION - new format now available!

SKINS
By Gavin Watson

Stunning collection of over 150 black and white photos of
skinheads during the 2 Tone and Oi! days, all taken by a
skinhead who is now a professional photographer.

SKINHEAD NATION
By George Marshall

Companion book to Spirit Of '69 that takes you on a guided tour
of today's skinhead world. Includes chapters on skinheads in
Britain, Europe and the USA, as well as on violence, and the
media. Includes over 100 previously unpublished photos.

**The above books are available from selected outlets and can
be ordered from most bookshops. If you have any
problems, please write to the address below for our full mail
order catalogue and an order form.**
S.T. Publishing
P.O. Box 12, Lockerbie, Dumfriesshire. DG11 3BW. Scotland.

BOSS SOUNDS - Classic Skinhead Reggae
By Marc Grifffiths

The first ever reference guide to skinhead reggae - so-called because when reggae first arrived in the UK in the late Sixties, it was the skinheads who took it to their hearts. Includes information on artists like Desmond Dekker and Laurel Aitken, producers like Duke Reid and Sir Coxsone, and labels like Trojan and Pama. Also includes a Top 300 of collectable reggae records from 1967-1973.

YOU'RE WONDERING NOW
- A History Of The Specials
By Paul Williams

For the first time, a detailed book that charts the rise of The Specials, and then follows the careers of band members after they spilt in 1981. Includes information on The Fun Boy Three, The Colour Field, The Special AKA, Terry Hall and more. With complete Specials discography.

THE TWO TONE STORY
By George Marshall

A completely updated version of the book that told the story of 2 Tone Records, from its humble beginnings in Coventry with the pre-Specials through the glory years of number one singles to the label's demise. Comes with full UK discography and plenty of new photos.

The above books are available from selected outlets and can be ordered from most bookshops. If you have any problems, please write to the address below for our full mail order catalogue and an order form.
S.T. Publishing
P.O. Box 12, Lockerbie, Dumfriesshire. DG11 3BW. Scotland.

ENGLAND BELONGS TO ME
By Steve Goodman

It's 1977. The safety pin is a fashion accessory. The swastika something far more dangerous. Derek Peterson is just another bored teenager, hanging around street corners in the Queen's Jubilee year. While everyone is screaming anarchy, Derek tries to stay true to his skinhead roots. But it's easier said than done when he meets a punk bird called Suzi. Together they take a brutal rollercoaster ride through the underground world of punk rock and extremist politics, where the only law is that of the urban jungle. The only justice, an eye for an eye, a tooth for a tooth.

SATURDAY'S HEROES
By Joe Mitchell

Paul West and his skinhead crew don't care what others think of them. They live in a violent world that sees them do battle with casual gangs, other skinheads and rival football supporters. A world that is slowly torn apart by aggro, a certain girl and betrayal. Pulp fiction in the tradition of Richard Allen.

ONE FOR THE ROAD
By Kid Stoker

Kid Stoker of punk outfit Red London weighs in with his debut novel about ageing punk band, The Outlaws, as they set out in a Ford Transit van for one final tour of the pubs and clubs of Europe.

The above books are available from selected outlets and can be ordered from most bookshops. If you have any problems, please write to the address below for our full mail order catalogue and an order form.
S.T. Publishing
P.O. Box 12, Lockerbie, Dumfriesshire. DG11 3BW. Scotland.